TWAYNE'S WORLD AUTHORS SERIES

A Survey of the World's Literature

Sylvia E. Bowman, Indiana University

GENERAL EDITOR

FRANCE

Maxwell A. Smith, Guerry Professor of French, Emeritus
The University of Chattanooga
Former Visiting Professor in Modern Languages
The Florida State University

EDITOR

Buffon

(*TWAS 243*)

TWAYNE'S WORLD AUTHORS SERIES (TWAS)

The purpose of TWAS is to survey the major writers —novelists, dramatists, historians, poets, philosophers, and critics—of the nations of the world. Among the national literatures covered are those of Australia, Canada, China, Eastern Europe, France, Germany, Greece, India, Italy, Japan, Latin America, the Netherlands, New Zealand, Poland, Russia, Scandinavia, Spain, and the African nations, as well as Hebrew, Yiddish, and Latin Classical literatures. This survey is complemented by Twayne's United States Authors Series and English Authors Series.

The intent of each volume in these series is to present a critical-analytical study of the works of the writer; to include biographical and historical material that may be necessary for understanding, appreciation, and critical appraisal of the writer and to present all material in clear, concise English—but not to vitiate the scholarly content of the work by doing so.

Buffon

By OTIS E. FELLOWS

Columbia University

AND

STEPHEN F. MILLIKEN

Rocky Mountain College

Twayne Publishers, Inc.   ::   New York

Preface

There are a good many quotation marks in this book and for
various reasons. Some of them enclose lengthy citations from
Buffon. These were necessary because Buffon's work is not available in modern English translation, not even in excerpts. In almost
all cases, the translations are our own. Often quotation marks are
used simply to indicate that the ordinary meanings of ordinary
words cannot be trusted in this context. These were necessary
because most of the basic concepts of science have changed since
Buffon's time, but much of the basic terminology has not.

Some of Buffon's ideas, outlined here, are amusing, because so
much of the science of the past strikes us as funny, but there was
no intention of making Buffon a figure of fun, merely to present
the full scope of his ideas, for to select only those that still make
the correct impression would be to distort his meaning, to dismiss
as negligible important aspects of his thought—without in any
way adding to his stature. When one succeeds in seeing the
problems Buffon attempted to solve in the precise terms that he
saw them—restoring the precise set of "givens" the problems had
for the eighteenth-century intellect—one can only be impressed
(sometimes awed) by the validity of the solutions Buffon has
offered.

The thought of a man of the past who was also a complete man
—and Buffon was that—should always be of some interest. The
reader must judge for himself whether that interest is properly
"literary" in Buffon's case. This is a dilemma that the modern
reader faces in approaching the work of any major figure of the
French Enlightenment. As a whole, the period judged science,
the "new Science" as they called it, to be of literary interest. It
is hoped that this book will be helpful to readers who are trying
to understand that point of view.

References to Buffon's letters are not footnoted when the information given in the text suffices for a specific letter to be identified without difficulty either in Henri Nadault de Buffon's editions of the *Correspondance de Buffon* or in the *Bibliographie de Buffon* contained in the volume devoted to Buffon in the series *Corpus Général des Philosophes Français* published by the Presses Universitaires de France in 1954.

References to Buffon's *Histoire Naturelle* are given in abbreviation in parentheses in the text rather than in the notes at the end. The same abbreviations are used in listing each volume of the *Histoire Naturelle* in the Chronology. Buffon's "work" was in fact many works with one title, and it is hoped that this procedure will aid the reader in relating the particular sections quoted to specific periods of Buffon's career. The references are to the original edition in quarto printed at the Imprimerie Royale in Paris, on the view that this is still the definitive edition. It was printed in enormous numbers and is still readily available to scholars at all major research libraries. The many, many later complete editions were all subjected, to some extent, to "scientific" editing; that is, the *Histoire Naturelle* was primarily regarded as a scientific work and efforts were made to bring it up to date. The abbreviations for the different sections of the *Histoire Naturelle* are as follows:

H.N. . . . . *Histoire Naturelle, Générale et Particulière*
H.N.O. . . . . . *Histoire Naturelle des Oiseaux* (ornithology)
H.N.M. . . . . . *Histoire Naturelle des Minéraux* (mineralogy)
H.N.S. . . . . . *Supplément à l'Histoire Naturelle.*

Acknowledgments

I express my gratitude to the John Simon Guggenheim Founda-
tion and the American Philosophical Society for giving me the
opportunity to carry out research on Buffon in France.

OTIS E. FELLOWS

I would like to thank Rocky Mountain College for a summer
travel grant in Europe and for a year's sabbatical leave, both devoted in large part to this study.

STEPHEN F. MILLIKEN

Contents

Preface

Chronology

1. Introduction   15
2. Diverse Faces of Buffon   28
3. Youth   40
4. Rise to Fame   51
5. Genesis Revised—From Seven Days to Seven Epochs   66
6. The Life Force   86
7. A Precursor of Darwin?   112
8. The Nature of Man   125
9. "Le Style Est l'Homme Même"   148

Notes and References   171

Selected Bibliography   179

Index   183

Chronology

1707   Georges-Louis Leclerc born in Montbard, September 7. His mother, Christine Marlin Leclerc, supervises his early education.

1714   Death of a maternal uncle enriches his family.

1720–1725   Studies at the Jesuit Collège des Godrans in Dijon.

1726   Completes the *licence* at the Faculté de Dijon and passes examinations in the law in July.

1728–1730   Medical and botanical studies at Angers.

1730–1732   Grand Tour through France and Italy in the company of the Duke of Kingston and Nathan Hickman. Death of his mother, in August, 1731. Establishes residence in Paris.

1733   Financial settlement with his father gives him control of his personal fortune, the family house in Montbard, and the village of Buffon. Begins extensive renovation of the house. Enters the Académie Royale des Sciences. Submits the first of the twenty-one papers or reports he was to submit to the Académie between 1733 and 1748, many later republished in the *Suppléments* to the *Histoire Naturelle*. Commences silviculture experiments.

1734   Begins to use the name *Buffon*. Establishes a tree nursery, his first major business venture.

1735   Translates Stephen Hales's *Vegetable Staticks*.

1739   Appointed Superintendent of the Jardin du Roi.

1740   Translates a treatise on calculus by Sir Isaac Newton. Becomes a Fellow of the Royal Society of London.

1747   Wins fame through burning mirror experiments, in imitation of Archimedes.

1748   Organic molecule experiments with John Turberville Needham.

1749   H.N. I, II, III (containing the *Théorie de la Terre* and the *Histoire Naturelle de l'Homme*).

1751   Avoids ecclesiastical censure.

1752   Marriage to Marie-Françoise de Saint-Belin.

1753   H.N. IV. Enters the Académie Française; delivers the *Discours sur le Style*.

1755   H.N. V.

1756   H.N. VI.

1758   H.N. VII. Birth of a daughter, in May, who died in October, 1759.

1760   H.N. VIII.

1761   H.N. IX.

1763   H.N. X.

1764   H.N. XI; H.N. XII. Birth of his son, Georges-Louis-Marie, nicknamed Buffonet.

1765   H.N. XIII.

1766   H.N. XIV.

1767   H.N. XV. Establishes an ironworks in the village of Buffon, his biggest business venture.

1769   Death of his wife.

1770   H.N.O. I.

1771   H.N.O. II. Nearly fatal illness; the succession to the superintendency of the Jardin du Roi is transferred from Buffon's son to the Count d'Angeviller.

1772   Buffon's lands are "elevated" to the status of a county, and Buffon becomes a count.

1774   H.N.S. I. Conciliation with Voltaire. Beginning of his friendship with Mme Necker.

1775   H.N.O. III; H.N.S. II.

1776   H.N.S. III.

1777   H.N.S. IV (containing the *Essai d'Arithmétique Morale*). A statue of Buffon is erected at the Jardin du Roi.

1778   H.N.O. IV; H.N.O. V; H.N.S. V (containing the *Epoques de la Nature*).

1779   H.N.O. VI.

1780   H.N.O. VII.

1781   H.N.O. VIII.

1782   H.N.S. VI.

1783   H.N.O. IX; H.N.M. I; H.N.M. II.

1784   Marriage of his son.

Chronology

1785   H.N.M. III. Visit of Hérault de Séchelles to Montbard.
1786   H.N.M. IV.
1788   H.N.M. V. Death of Buffon on April 16.
1789   H.N.S. VII. The Count de Lacépède undertakes the continuation of the *Histoire Naturelle*.

CHAPTER 1

Introduction

I *Fickle Fame*

WESTERN civilization has known few men of letters and even fewer scientists who were as singularly honored during their lives as France's Georges-Louis Leclerc, comte de Buffon, scientist and belletrist, whose published work seemed to lay claim to science as a new branch of the humanities. So unimpeded was his rise to fame, so great the weight of his authority, so imposing his very presence, that few among his contemporaries dared to attack him frankly and openly. It seemed far easier to honor him, and he was showered with honors.

While still alive, he saw a statue of himself unveiled in the public gardens of the world's greatest capital city—an unusual distinction then as now. Several of Europe's most powerful monarchs sent him expensive personal gifts, and distinguished travelers from many nations made pilgrimages to his estate in Burgundy. On one such visit, in 1770, Jean-Jacques Rousseau, a giant of the age, knelt in homage at the threshold of Buffon's study. During England's numerous wars with France, British privateers boarding French ships in search of booty made certain that packing cases of zoological or botanical specimens addressed to "M. de Buffon, Paris," reached their destination. The academies of arts and sciences of Europe and America eagerly sought his membership— even the august, traditionally reserved Académie Française. As superintendent of the Jardin du Roi, the eighteenth-century equivalent of what today would be called a great research institute, he had total command over the varied facilities of that famous establishment.

His multi-volumed *Histoire Naturelle, Générale et Particulière* was published, with no initial cost to himself, on the royal presses of the realm. Studies of the holdings of eighteenth-century private libraries reveal that the work became one of the century's greatest

"best sellers," and the number of editions is equally indicative of
uncommon success. In addition to the princeps edition in quarto
printed at the Imprimerie Royale, Buffon launched six other
editions during his lifetime, two in quarto, one in octavo, and
three in duodecimo; in all, there have been fifty-two complete
editions of the huge work in French, eight in German, six in
Italian, four in English, one in Spanish, one in Dutch, and more
than 325 partial editions in these various languages. Owing in
part to income derived from the editions under his control, in part
to other commercial ventures similarly dependent on government
patronage, Buffon became an extremely wealthy man.

When, in his eighty-first year, he died at his sumptuous apartments in Paris, he was almost a legendary figure. Immense crowds,
perhaps twenty thousand people, thronged the narrow streets of
the city to follow his funeral cortege. Periodicals of the day repeated the refrain that the last of the four great French literary
figures of the century was dead, and that, as the British *Gentleman's Magazine* put it, "the four bright lamps," Montesquieu,
Voltaire, Rousseau, and Buffon, were now "totally extinguished."
The copper coffin-plate of Georges-Louis Leclerc, the great-grand-
son of a peasant—though this he would never have avowed—bore
the following inscription, with all his resounding (and recently
acquired) titles: "Comte de Buffon, Seigneur de Montbard, Marquis de Rougemont, Vicomte de Quincy, Seigneur de La Mairie,
Les Harans, Les Berges et autres lieux."

Almost three-quarters of a century later the distinguished critic
Charles-Augustin Sainte-Beuve wrote: "Buffon, the last to die of
the four great men of the 18th century, in a sense brought that
century to a close the day of his death, April 16, 1788." Nineteenth-
century French literary histories traditionally devoted a full
chapter to Buffon. His reputation, his position as a major figure,
it would seem, had stood the test of time—for a century. Yet, in
the volumes devoted to the eighteenth century (IV, 1951; IV
Supplement, 1968) in the currently standard critical bibliography
of French literature published by the Syracuse University Press
under the general editorship of D. C. Cabeen the sections devoted
to Diderot, Voltaire, and Rousseau all contain more than 500
entries, those on Montesquieu 240, and the total for Buffon is
only 62—clear indication that, in the twentieth century, Buffon
has slipped to the status of a minor figure. Anthologies of the

literature of the period now sometimes omit him entirely or, at most, grant him a few pages. In recent years, though, there has been something of a revival of interest in Buffon, a countertrend —several volumes of Buffon studies, for example, were published in France in the 1950's, one with a complete, and impressive, scholarly bibliography—but it is doubtful that critics will ever again begin essays on him, as did Sainte-Beuve in the *Causeries du Lundi*, by invoking *"l'importance des questions soulevées et encore agitées autour du grand nom de Buffon."* The questions remain, but they are now rarely associated with this once gigantic figure of the French Enlightenment.

II *Buffon's World—and Relevancy*

Literature mythologizes and science demythologizes. Such is the modern view. Literature offers a world humanized, reshaped to order by man's creative imagination, while science deals only with "hard facts" and cold, mathematical abstractions, with no concern whatsoever for the comfort of the human psyche. An immense abyss seems to separate these disciplines, and modern man, inhabitant of a world transformed by science, dominated by science and with only meager tolerance for the poeticizing imagination, views with suspicion any attempt to bring them together. And Buffon's work represented, not a simple confrontation of science and literature, but an unparalleled, virtually complete intermixture of the two. He is the only important scientist ever to have achieved the rank of a major literary figure almost entirely through his original scientific publications. He was not simply a popularizer of scientific thought; he was concerned, rather, with presenting directly to the general reading public scientific theories which he himself had devised, in a style distinguished by its power and beauty. These facts alone seem sufficient to explain the recent change in Buffon's reputation. There was never a determined process of debunking. His style retains its luster. And, after all, much of the greatest literature of the French eighteenth century is not in the form of plays, poems, or novels, but in informative essays. Yet he was not a "man for all seasons," as were to some extent Voltaire, Montesquieu, and Rousseau, and, above all, Diderot, who has taken Buffon's place among the "Big Four"; in his single-minded drive for success, his determination to captivate his contemporaries, Buffon identified himself too completely with a particular moment in time, and that moment has passed. Voltaire, Montesquieu, Rousseau, Diderot, and a host of minor figures devoted substantial portions of their writings to science; Buffon alone devoted almost his entire production to it, and his work was thus subject to the same pattern of inevitable obsolescence that characterizes the history of science itself.

Still we cannot fully understand the period of the Enlightenment, or its literature, without him. Basically, the Enlightenment was an effort to shed new light on social problems, human problems in general, by applying to them insights derived from the New Science of Bacon, Descartes, Newton, and Locke. This intellectual movement is often represented on the cover designs of books on the period as a burning torch held aloft, dispersing the cobwebs and dark shadows of the past; that torch was science, not the science of today, our science, but science as Buffon understood it, a science in which man's creative imagination still played a major part. If we approach important Enlightenment figures, such as the Founding Fathers of the American Republic, men like Franklin and Jefferson and Adams, without some knowledge of the special nature of the eighteenth-century science that shaped their thought, our impressions of them must inevitably be distorted. We see them, falsely, as being, in all essential points, men of our own time. Buffon is, of course, not our only avenue of approach to eighteenth-century scientific thought; the period abounded in scientific works, but his were the most readable, the most complete, and more than any others, with the possible exception of Diderot's, they show the creative imagination openly at work.

We usually think of a writer as interesting by virtue of the richness and diversity of his character and interests, his ability to touch us directly through something eternal in his concerns, but a writer may also be interesting by virtue of his limitations, if he lived at a time that interests us and if his limitations sprang primarily from a successful effort to identify himself totally with that time. Without denying that there is often in Buffon's writing that "something eternal," brief glimpses of a fascinating individuality that was seldom exposed, we must recognize that, both in style and thought, his writing incarnated to an exceptional degree the idiom of his age.

Every age of great changes is also an age of great explainers.

Explaining does help; it is easier to master a new experience or a new environment if there is someone there attempting to reduce the whole to precise verbal formulations: a teacher, a critic, a tour guide, a philosopher, a Marx, a Freud, a Tillich, or a Buffon. The explainers need not be totally correct; they must seem correct, but a relation to what people want to hear, to what relieves their fears, their uneasiness before the new, is more important. These great explainers enjoy immense popularity and prestige in their own time, but following cycles tend to deal harshly with them. A Duns Scotus becomes a dunce; a Buffon, as George Bernard Shaw reported in the preface to *Back to Methuselah*, may come to be referred to as "the celebrated Buffoon."

Buffon reached manhood at a time when the new ideological currents were just beginning to effect profound changes in the traditional modes of thought in France. Cartesian methodical doubt was fast demolishing many of the long respected positions supported by neo-Aristotelian authority, by the "science" of theology along with organized religion, and even by superstitions venerable with age. There were also the rational a priori ideas in the Cartesian tradition which themselves helped clear the air of outworn systems while offering new, often fruitful ones in their place; Descartes' own emphasis on matter in motion as a basic creative principle for the world of being might be considered one of these. Then too, there was an ever-increasing insistence upon the somewhat narrower experimental a posteriori approach in the Baconian-Newtonian tradition that in the last half of the seventeenth century served as a guiding principle for the Royal Society of London and, early in the eighteenth century, swept across the Channel to shake the very foundations of the newly established Académie Royale des Sciences in Paris. Along with these intellectual drives came John Locke's philosophy of sensationalism which, with Voltaire's *Lettres Philosophiques* in 1734, gave Frenchmen of a speculative turn of mind a fresh awareness of man qua man, in relation to himself, his fellow men, and the world within reach of his senses. There was in Buffon's own intellectual formation a fusion of all three currents: Cartesian rationalism, Baconian-Newtonian experimentalism, and Locke's sensationalism. Buffon's thought was both original and systematic and, at the same time, highly eclectic. It is not surprising therefore that his thought, like that of all his contempo-

raries, was at times marked by curious inconsistencies and startling antinomies.

The scientific "facts" that Buffon offers us in the *Histoire
Naturelle* are, of course, often wrong, sometimes even comically
wrong, but this does not automatically invalidate the basic assumptions with which he approached them. Like Descartes and,
indeed, Newton himself—Buffon's great idol—Buffon assumed
that the facts of science could be finally "explained," reduced to
a coherent system. Today, in a time of reassessment of scientific
approaches with a new emphasis on the value of theoretical
models, this view seems less *démodé* than it did a few years back.

Perhaps of all his contemporaries the one that Buffon most
resembled was Montesquieu. Montesquieu's *Esprit des Lois* was
an attempt to reveal a system of logically consistent patterns
underlying the laws of man, and Buffon's *Histoire Naturelle*
sought to reveal similar patterns, a comparable simplicity and
order—even a like congruence with the character of man—in the
laws of nature. Like Montesquieu, Buffon judged it expedient to
advance his daring hypotheses and still more daring syntheses
little by little, step by step, in the course of an immensely detailed work that was the result of many years of arduous labor.
Yet Montesquieu's theoretical patterns are still exciting, still stim-
ulating, for legal concepts evolve slowly, and Buffon's seem exciting only when restored to their historical context, but this last
is perhaps too hasty a judgment.

All Buffon's theories depart from and return to a single point:
man. Only in relation to man was anything of direct influence
to Buffon. This made him, among other things, an ecologist:

. . . despite continual losses of these residues of living nature, nature's
productive capacity is so great that the quantity of this vegetal humus
would continue to augment everywhere if we did not despoil and im-
poverish the earth by our planned exploitations of it, which are almost
always immoderate. (H.N.M. I, *"De la Terre Végétale"*)

The catholicity of the interests of the Enlightenment thinker, his
overall concern with a "natural" order of things in which man
should be fully at ease, made it almost inevitable that he should
be an ecologist, a point of view to which we are just now returning. The reader of Buffon does find excitement in his views—even

when by no means acceptable—and also a new awareness that there are fashions in scientific thought too, and that the pendulum swings both to and fro. Buffon mocked the medieval alchemists because they thought they could sway nature out of her customary paths, ignoring the immensity of her power (H.N.M. III, *"Du Mercure"*), but scientists of more modern times, post-Buffonian scientists, long subscribed to views similarly arrogant.

Buffon, the spokesman of his time, poses the challenge of a variety of scientific thought that does not isolate science but links it intimately to all other realms of human thought and to man's most basic needs. He was audacious—the central slogan of the Enlightenment was Kant's *sapere aude,* "Dare to know"—daring even to present the facts of nature as cogs in a system that was the product of his own mind, born of his confidence in his own intuitive grasp of the way it must be. We may not be ready yet to give credence to the thought of a "scientist" who grants himself the imaginative freedom of a metaphysician or a poet, who, in fact, at times even mythologizes, but, if nothing else, he can give us a firmer understanding of his times, and some pleasure.

III *Buffon's Work*

Buffon's monumental *Histoire Naturelle, Générale et Particulière,* his one great work, was the principal commercial rival of Diderot's thirty-five volume *Encyclopédie,* the most impressive publishing venture of the age, and the two have often been compared. Like the *Encyclopédie,* the *Histoire Naturelle* was a vast repository of authenticated fact that remained in use as a general reference work long after the death of its compiler. It differed from the *Encyclopédie,* however, in that the presentation of factual data was everywhere subordinated to the steady unfolding of a singularly unified world view. Buffon, like Diderot, employed collaborators, but only a few and never on a basis of equality; their contributions, by their own efforts and his editing, were transformed into pastiches of his style; the guiding ideas were always his. The *Encyclopédie* was a team effort, given a measure of unity by the organizing genius of Diderot; the *Histoire Naturelle,* despite assistance received, was entirely Buffon's.

In the early 1740's, following his appointment as superintendent of the Jardin du Roi in Paris, Buffon undertook the preparation of an analytical and descriptive catalogue of the Jardin's already

extensive collection of botanical and zoological specimens, and
this *catalogue raisonné* shortly developed into the *Histoire
Naturelle.* The first three volumes were published in 1749. By 1788,
the year of his death and only a few months before the outbreak
of the French Revolution, thirty-five of the massive quarto volumes of the princeps edition of this work had already appeared,
but the final volume of this edition, the forty-fourth, was not published by his successors until 1804. So broad, so "literary" was
Buffon's conception of his subject that he was able to include
almost everything that he wrote during this period within the
flexible format of the *Histoire Naturelle,* so that that vast production was at the same time a single, relatively unified work and,
so to speak, the collected works of Buffon. The thirty-five volumes he himself saw through the press included three general
introductory volumes, twelve volumes on mammals, nine volumes
on birds, five volumes on minerals, and six volumes entitled *Suppléments.*

In the more general essays Buffon digressed freely, touching
upon (or discussing at considerable length) a variety of moral,
social, theological, and philosophical questions that have little
obvious connection to natural history: improvements needed in
contemporary education; the proper manner of caring for infants;
the degree to which the soul might be said to control those no-
toriously troublesome parts of the body, the organs of generation;
the relative unimportance of fashions in choosing clothing and
wigs; the limitations set on human knowledge; the several reasons
we have for not fearing death. In the volumes of *Suppléments*
he published, in addition to actual supplements to articles in the
earlier volumes, some rather miscellaneous early memoirs, many
dating from the 1730's, and the discourses, generally on literary
topics, he had delivered before the Académie Française, including the period's most celebrated discussion of neoclassical literary
theory, Buffon's famous *Discours sur le Style,* and an enthusiastic
review of recent innovations in the French theater. On the whole,
however, the *Histoire Naturelle* was devoted to matters more
suitable for presentation to the Académie Royale des Sciences, of
which Buffon was perpetual treasurer, such as accounts of experiments he himself had performed (some of which were highly
spectacular), extended descriptions of specimens gathered from
the four corners of the earth; general, definitive descriptive ac-

counts of mammals, birds, and minerals; and the exposition of theories concerning the probable interrelationships of the phenomena described.

Even his contemporaries found it difficult to classify this sprawling, heterogeneous mass of essays, to fit it into any easily recognizable category. His ability to extract glittering, crystal clear generalizations from swarms of data suggested to many a resemblance to Plato. His meticulous, almost obsessive attention to literary style and his lifelong concern with explaining the "nature of things" recall, somewhat more forcefully, the Roman philosopher poet Lucretius, author of *De Rerum Natura*. In the eighteenth century, however, he was most often compared to another eminent Roman, Pliny the Elder, and, to his immense satisfaction, he was widely known as "the French Pliny," but his work was not in any sense, like Pliny's, a digest of earlier compendia; the technical material presented in the *Histoire Naturelle* usually represented extensive research conducted by Buffon himself or by one of his many assistants, secretaries, collaborators, or *correspondants* (the latter was an official title he was authorized to confer on amateurs throughout the world who aided him in a substantial way). His privileged position, the breadth of his interests, recall Aristotle, and this too was a comparison often made. Almost always, though, the comparisons were to the ancients. In a neoclassical age, the magnitude of his work, its singleness of purpose, shining through a great diversity of matter, its disregard of modern genre classifications, its imaginative power—all made him seem authentically classical.

IV   *Masks and Unity*

"When I appear on the world's great stage," wrote Descartes, in a much quoted Latin fragment, "I am masked." By Buffon's time, a century later, masks were practically *de rigueur* for thoughtful Continental writers, and the role of the *philosophe masqué* was no longer a novelty. With few exceptions, in France and elsewhere on the Continent throughout the eighteenth century the aims and achievements of the age's more daring thinkers came into unremitting conflict with the disintegrating yet still effectively oppressive authority of both church and throne. Voltaire, Diderot, Helvétius, D'Holbach, Rousseau, and others were, despite the public admiration for their works, insurgents against

imposed traditions, constantly obliged to have recourse to a wide
variety of subterfuges. The dangers faced, though not those of
a modern police state, were quite real. Voltaire and Rousseau
were hounded into exile by the authorities, Diderot actually imprisoned for a time, and Montesquieu, despite the prestige of his
social and judicial rank, saw his *Esprit des Lois* placed on the
Index of Prohibited Books.

Buffon's *Histoire Naturelle,* a work rich in new ideas, every
one of them based on logic and physical evidence alone, clearly
places him in the center of the Enlightenment camp, a remarkably hazardous position, yet, unlike his great contemporaries, he
escaped all penalties and enjoyed throughout his life the privileged position of a high government official and an aristocrat.
This singularity has given rise to one of the many controversies
that have divided Buffon scholars: Were the subterfuges he employed, his personal "mask," uncommonly effective or did he,
despite appearances to the contrary, actually support *ancien régime* traditions?

Buffon was assiduous in his formal religious observances, swift
to make the compromises demanded by authority. In 1751, for
example, the *Histoire Naturelle* was threatened with censure by
the faculty of theology of the University of Paris, the redoubtable
Sorbonne. In a letter to his self-appointed judges, later published
in the *Histoire Naturelle* (H.N. IV), Buffon stated that he had
presented his "hypothesis" on the formation of the planets "only
as a pure philosophical speculation," and the Sorbonne fully
accepted this "disavowal," with some encouragement from Buffon's supporters in the government, to the considerable surprise
of Buffon himself. It is a standard statement, employed in similar
circumstances by many other Enlightenment figures, and the nature and bulk of the *Histoire Naturelle* effectively refute it: it is
surely very difficult to believe that Buffon devoted his entire life
to the exposition and documentation of a system of ideas he believed in his heart to be nothing more than sterile and unreal
speculation, as a harmless aristocratic amusement. Yet there have
always been eminent scholars, archconservatives in politics, who
have claimed that in his case such disavowals are not to be
doubted, that he offered them too easily, too confidently, too successfully, for them to be thought other than sincere.

This particular controversy is typical of many that have arisen among interpreters of Buffon, who is at the same time one of the clearest and most consistent writers in any literature and one of the most argued over. These controversies cannot be dismissed altogether, but neither do they warrant prolonged attention in a study of this type. Buffon's work was not an exercise in self-revelation; his private life, his private personality, were almost completely "masked," and in these areas the critic can only speculate, and interpretations will differ, but the masks employed to guard his work from suppression do not constitute a real difficulty. Almost always, in the controversies that involve his printed statements, one side appears to be motivated by personal interests that have little to do with the desire to see Buffon clearly, and to be massing flimsy and specious arguments, paper tigers, against the obvious. Buffon did resort to the stock subterfuges of the embattled Enlightenment thinkers. Only then could he feel assured of the freedom to write and to publish, to make what he considered must be a vital, immensely important contribution to man's struggle to understand and master the forces of nature, the central Enlightenment ideal. But he never permitted these pious and politic protestations—routinely reiterated and always out of context—to obscure in any way the presentation of his thought. Approached without preconceptions, Buffon's meaning is never in doubt.

In modern terms, perhaps, Buffon's concern for his social and official position would mark him as a conservative, but modern terms do not apply. The tendency to expect the views of major Enlightenment thinkers to closely resemble those of twentieth-century liberals and radicals is an example of a preconception to avoid. The men who laid down the intellectual foundations for the French Revolution were rarely revolutionaries themselves. Theirs were the utopias of reasonable and practical men. They believed that a more "natural" order of things must be restored— and in this respect Buffon was clearly an Enlightenment thinker —but for the most part they did not believe that the existing order would have to be shattered to accomplish this. Once the generality of mankind had been brought to see things clearly and truly as they are, once men had been "enlightened," they felt, the necessary changes must follow in due course, easily and without violence. Their immediate concern was with ordered and accurate thought, and few among them were aware that that is a potentially explosive commodity.

A more substantial mask than those adopted to ward off suppression is constituted by Buffon's efforts to conceal the evolution of his thought throughout the period, almost half a century, that he devoted to writing the *Histoire Naturelle*. To maintain the marketability of all of the *Histoire Naturelle,* of the earlier as well as of the later volumes, since the total work continued to be offered to the public as a unit, he protested often that nothing of fundamental importance had been changed and he chose to issue volumes of supplements rather than to revise the earlier volumes. It is an impressive indication of the actual degree of continuity in his thought that these efforts were, on the whole, successful, and that many of his commentators through the years have assumed in discussing his ideas that they were changeless throughout his career.

No man's thinking was ever more unified, more of a piece, than Buffon's. Jacques Roger has demonstrated in his critical edition of Buffon's essay *Les Epoques de la Nature* that the explanation of the differences between the cosmogony Buffon offered in 1749 in the essay *La Théorie de la Terre* and the definitive cosmogony he presented in 1779 in *Les Epoques de la Nature* is to be found in large part in the biological studies he had undertaken in the interim. Equally striking interconnections between seemingly distinct fields of investigation may be noted throughout the *Histoire Naturelle:* Buffon's early speculations concerning the nature of mathematical truth, and its remoteness from pragmatic truth contributed to his rejection of Linnaeus's early system of classification as too neatly mechanical for application to living things; conclusions reached in his youthful theorizing in the field of ballistics reappeared in his first cosmogony; his experiments in optics led into a study of the eye and then of the organs of sensation in general; his theory of the primary importance of lucid thought in literary style, that is, conclusions and a plan of development arrived at before the actual writing is begun, is reflected in the manner in which he at times conducted scientific experiments, parting from, and usually returning to, an a priori position. Similarly, his scientific activities often found secondary expression in practical business enterprises: his botanical studies led to ventures in tree nurseries, and his experiments with fused minerals to the ownership of a foundry. It is highly impractical to attempt to isolate a small segment of Buffon's work for individual study. The inadequacy of any such attempt, the fragmentary character of the material studied, would be immediately apparent. The original premises and the ultimate conclusions would always lie just out of reach, beyond the limits set up for the study.

It is in Buffon's own remarkable consistency that we have sought the unifying principle of the present study, although a serious attempt has been made to note as well the occasional contradictions and some of the progressive changes in his thought. Buffon's consistency extended even to the events of his life. His severely disciplined private life and his career, that long and even advance from provincial bourgeois to great public figure, were as much the products of his will and his *idées maîtresses* as was the *Histoire Naturelle* itself. The major purpose of this study has been to define these *idées maîtresses*—these dominating concepts —succinctly and, hopefully, in terms meaningful to the modern reader, and to attempt to suggest their relevance, and importance, to the intellectual life of the eighteenth century.

CHAPTER 2

Diverse Faces of Buffon

I The Public Image—The Manner of a French Marshal

AT the height of his career Buffon unabashedly affected the grand manner. In a private letter in December, 1765, the Scottish philosopher David Hume, at the time an official at the English embassy in Paris and a close personal friend of the author of the *Histoire Naturelle,* briefly characterized Buffon: "who in his Figure and Air and Deportment answers your idea of a Mareschal of France rather than of a Philosopher." [1] Among the *philosophes,* D'Alembert in particular, Buffon was often referred to as "le comte de Tuffière" (roughly, "Count Allproud") after a character in the Destouches play *Le Glorieux.* For the average French reader it is this aspect of Buffon, the self-conscious magnifico, that most readily comes to mind, much as the average English reader is apt to picture Dr. Johnson pontificating at the Mitre coffeehouse or Lord Byron in a lady's boudoir.

In the case of Buffon, however, it is difficult for a biographer to add much humanizing detail to the traditional silhouette. Buffon's "image" was very definitely a conscious creation. It was as a man of triumphs, not as a man of struggles, that he desired to be remembered. He rose to fame from origins that were obscure in the extreme in an age when such a rise was regarded as something to be concealed rather than as a cause for congratulation, and he provided his prospective biographers with only the scantiest details on the period preceding his fame, emphasizing always his great successes, the honors heaped upon him.

In fact, he seems even to have falsified a few details concerning his youth. The resultant biographical problems have never been fully resolved, and there exists no full-scale scholarly biography of Buffon. There are, though, a number of contemporary biographical memoirs that provide vivid portraits of the mature Buffon, the aging grandee of science and literature. Moreover,

Buffon's great-grandnephew, Henri Nadault de Buffon, brought together in two editions of Buffon's correspondence (1860, 1885) an impressive array of undigested biographical data, much of it bearing on the early years, as well as 639 letters written by Buffon over a period stretching from his early twenties to just before his death at the age of eighty. A number of additional letters have since been printed in scholarly journals or are now easily available in microfilms of the manuscripts that can be ordered from the libraries where they are deposited.[2]

This treasure trove of biographical material is not, however, an unmixed blessing. Nadault de Buffon's work as editor was far from impeccable; twenty-two of the letters that had appeared in the 1860 edition of the *Correspondance de Buffon,* for example, reappeared in the 1885 edition with altered dates, without any notation being provided to explain the changes made. Nadault's only major failure as an editor, however, was the volume *Buffon, sa famille, ses collaborateurs et ses familiers* (1863); this was ostensibly the memoirs of Humbert-Bazile, one of the last of Buffon's secretaries, edited from the manuscript by Nadault, but it was in reality made up to a considerable extent of passages lifted from earlier works, such as the little known *Vie Privée du Comte de Buffon* (1788) of the Chevalier Aude, who had resided briefly with Buffon in a capacity somewhere between that of secretary and guest. Much of Aude's limited and leisurely work was devoted to Aude himself. In general, the accounts of contemporaries contradict one another on point after point, and in sum they reveal more about the men who wrote them than the man they were written about.

Buffon's extant letters are for the most part rather formal business documents, and where they are at all revealing or personal in tone they present as many faces of Buffon as there are correspondents addressed. Buffon was a master of the art of adapting the tone of a letter to the person he was writing to, though the shifts are always slight and never at odds with the public image. They present the great man at grips with the mundane and even trivial details of everyday life, but it is always the great man they present, the figure in the splendid portraits and statues. Buffon believed in the accuracy of his public image, and he wanted both contemporary and future generations to accept it without modification.

He was convinced that the masterly prose style of the *Histoire Naturelle,* so very different from that of the matter-of-fact, unlabored letters, somehow embodied his essence, and would transmit the essential Buffon to posterity. "The style is the man" is his most famous dictum, and the lordly manner of his mature years was as much a product of this style as was the elaborate, studied prose of the *Histoire Naturelle.*

II *Hérault's Portrait*

By far the best of the contemporary accounts of Buffon is Hérault de Séchelles' *Voyage à Montbard,* written in 1785 when Buffon was almost eighty, but still busily at work on the *Histoire Naturelle.*[3] Hérault's little book, a remarkable early example of the modern magazine profile, is the only document we have that penetrates beyond the popular image. Hérault spared his readers no scandalous detail, and his work has often been denounced by admirers of Buffon as an outrageous libel. Henri Nadault de Buffon listed among his motives for publishing his great ancestor's respectable correspondence a desire to destroy public confidence in Hérault's account and to restore to Buffon's image its pristine purity. Those who prefer to regard Hérault as reliable can take comfort from the fact that he seems to have remained on terms of intimacy with Buffon's circle long after the first publication of the profile. Eight years later he was one of the witnesses at the second marriage of Buffon's son. And Nadault de Buffon himself did not hesitate to borrow from Hérault's work, for the notes to his own *Correspondance de Buffon,* every detail that he did not find personally offensive.

Hérault's profile is loosely constructed, rambling, frequently repetitious, but it is also lively and highly readable. In 1785 Hérault was an ambitious young lawyer and journalist. He had made known to Buffon his desire to publish an account of his manner of life, and Buffon had sent him a pressing invitation to spend a few weeks at his residence in Montbard, where, for more than half a century, he spent the eight most pleasant months of every year at work on the *Histoire Naturelle,* reserving only the four winter months for the period of residence in Paris made necessary by his duties as superintendent of the Jardin du Roi.

Montbard, Buffon's birthplace, is a tiny city nestled in the Burgundian hills some forty miles to the northwest of Dijon. Even today the topography of Montbard bears eloquent testimony to the colossal egotism of its most famous citizen. In 1733, when Buffon came into possession of his family's spacious townhouse in Montbard, the town was dominated by the remnants of an enormous medieval fortress that covered the top of the large hill directly behind Buffon's residence. Buffon had promptly assumed full proprietary rights over the hill, on the flimsiest of legal grounds, and began to raze the already crumbling feudal fortifications, conserving only two of the towers, the chapel, and a miniature guardhouse. In a few years' time the top of the hill became a man-made plateau and here Buffon had constructed an elaborate formal neoclassical garden, "in the style of Versailles," to use a phrase of Stendhal's, one of the many tourists to visit the spot in later years.[4] With somewhat ostentatious makework largesse, Buffon had insisted that the soil needed for refilling the stony hilltop should be transported, with baskets and hods, by a small army of laborers, the indigent of the Montbard region. "It is," he piously remarked, "a way of distributing alms without encouraging laziness," and, less cheerfully in a much later conversation with his sister Mme Nadault, "You could entirely cover my gardens with six franc coins without coming close to the sums they cost me."[5] Montbard lost its splendid old fortress because Buffon was convinced that only in the most felicitous of surroundings could his impressive literary talents be exploited to the full, and to his mind this meant a sizable, private formal garden, with adjacent workrooms, all within easy walking distance of his manor house. During this same period he had also undertaken the renovation of the house itself, slowly converting it into an elegant baroque château. Today the sprawling château remains in use as a government office building and low-rent residence for civil servants, and the gardens on the hill are a public park. A statue of Buffon dominates the pocket-sized square in front of the house. The trees planted so long ago on the hilltop have grown huge and shaggy and the park—now a favorite retreat for romantic adolescents drawn by the thick shade of its luxuriant vegetation—is in no way suggestive of Versailles, but the peculiar flatness of the hilltop, its faint resemblance to a small aircraft carrier, is still a vaguely disquieting reminder of one man's singleness of purpose, and truly extraordinary egotism.

When Hérault de Séchelles arrived in Montbard after a hasty

coach trip from Paris, he learned to his dismay that the octo-
genarian Buffon was completely indisposed, due to one of his
periodic attacks of kidney stones, in such pain in fact that he
could see no one. Hérault was about to leave when Buffon sent
word that he was still eager for the visit, and that they would
fit the interviews into the intervals between the spasms of pain.
This circumstance does cast some shadows of doubt on Hérault's
study. It obliged him to rely less on conversations with Buffon
and more on local gossip than he had intended, and many of the
preconceptions he brought with him passed intact into his book.

The interviews did shake loose a few preconceptions, however. When Buffon walked into the anteroom where his youthful guest was awaiting his first audience, Hérault was amazed
to see a tall, erect, heavyset and muscular man who looked closer
to sixty than eighty, apparently in excellent health, his face be-
traying no signs of the agonies he had been enduring for days—
a mark, he was told by intimates, of Buffon's sturdy mental discipline, capable of surmounting all physical ills. Hérault was
struck by the resemblance to the bust by Houdon, despite the
old man 's thick black eyebrows and dark, almost jet black, eyes.
As on many occasions recorded in the book, he meticulously
noted Buffon's attire—an intricate, antiquated hair style, obviously freshly set by the curling irons of an expert hairdresser,
the hair snowy white, a sumptuous yellow dressing gown with
white stripes and a blue floral pattern. He noted too Buffon's
theatrical entrance, particularly the slow, deliberate turn to close
the door before advancing to meet his guest.

From the first, Hérault was impressed by his host's singularly
frank vanity. Asked immediately which of Buffon's writings he
had most recently read, Hérault named the *Vues sur la nature,*
and Buffon remarked, "There are in it passages of the most sublime eloquence." Vanity was the shortcoming Hérault commented
upon most often in his account of Buffon. Again and again he
was frankly flabbergasted by his host's serene confidence in his
own immortal genius. Advising Hérault to confine his reading
largely to the few, truly great writers that mankind has produced,
Buffon listed the five greatest as follows: "Newton, Bacon, Leibnitz, Montesquieu, and Myself." In the end Hérault was more
dazzled than amused by this trait. Buffon received a great deal
of fan mail from an admiring literary public, kept it all, and

showed much of it to Hérault. Confronted by several letters written to Buffon by Catherine the Great of Russia, filled with such
assurances as "Newton took the first step, you have taken the
second" and "You haven't yet emptied your pockets on the subject of Man," and a similar letter from Prince Henry of Prussia,
Hérault enthused, "Glory seemed to take on visible form before
my eyes; I felt that I could reach out and touch it, lay my hands
upon it, and this admiration from Crowned Heads, compelled to
bow down in this way before a greatness in no way specious,
pierced my heart, homage of superhuman proportions. . . ."

Other weaknesses, both major and minor, were not passed over
in silence, however, and the chronicler's list is long. With considerable surprise, Hérault learned that Buffon's conversation in
his hours of relaxation was often such that ladies present were
obliged by his *polissonneries* to leave the room in much haste
and some confusion. The celebrated prose stylist, he found too,
had no horror of slang and habitually punctuated his conversation with such *expressions négligées* as *pardieu* and *tout ça*.

More serious, Hérault described Buffon as so infatuated with
the exclusively carnal aspects of sexual love that he frequently
sought satisfaction with ladies of easy virtue and with girls of
extremely tender years procured by his servants, fearing the
sentimental involvements entailed in relationships with more sincere and more mature women. This was the one "calumny" that
Nadault de Buffon never challenged, perhaps regarding it as beneath his dignity. And this is unfortunate, because the statement
in all probability was a calumny, and a number of letters in
Nadault's *Correspondance de Buffon* bear witness to Buffon's romantic involvement with women who were definitely not *petites
filles*. The rumor of vicious sexual tastes was very possibly among
the preconceptions that Hérault brought with him to Montbard.
Such a rumor had need of no basis more substantial than the
long-standing misinterpretation of two passages in the *Histoire
Naturelle*, passages which had gained regrettable notoriety in
1749 and 1753. In the essay *De la Nature de l'Homme* (H.N. II)
Buffon had treated at considerable length, and with impressive
authority, the question of sexual responses in adolescent girls,
with the entirely laudable intention of clearing up a number of
old wives' tales and popular superstitions concerning the "signs
of virginity," an area where ignorance led often to domestic trag-

edy. His information was drawn largely from interviews with physicians and midwives. And, in the essay *Discours sur la Nature des Animaux* (H.N. IV), Buffon had argued that, although theologians assure us that animals have no soul, observation shows us that animals are capable, despite their unalloyed materiality, of experiencing all that is best in love, including self-sacrifice. His conclusion was that the best of love—since it is known to soulless creatures—must therefore be purely physical, or material —a conclusion that severely jolted many a reader. Mme de Pompadour expressed her disapprobation by swatting Buffon rather smartly with her fan when she encountered him at Versailles shortly after she had read the article. In the eighteenth century, as today, attempts to shed new light on the realm of sexual mores might result in nothing more than a sinister reputation for the reformer.

The gravest of Buffon's shortcomings catalogued by Hérault, in the opinion of many of Buffon's admirers, involved, not sex, but religion. Hérault presents Buffon as a conscious and cynical hypocrite in the matter of religious observances—scrupulously observing the forms, but only for the sake of public appearances and without the slightest vestige of inner conviction. This was Hérault's own position, and one widely attributed to Buffon, but so simple a position contrasts oddly with the complexity of the many passages in the *Histoire Naturelle* that touch in some way upon the subject of religion, in which elements of doubt and elements of faith occur with almost equal frequency. Hérault is convincing when he reports that Buffon described the document of submission he addressed to the Sorbonne in 1751 under threat of immediate censure as a *"persiflage."* He is still convincing when he records it as Buffon's view that it is possible to express any nuance of opinion without an overt break with the most rigidly orthodox dogma, provided the writer has sufficient ingenuity and is willing to insist periodically upon the remoteness of religious concerns from the mundane matters he is discussing. He is less convincing when he quotes Buffon as saying that in every passage of the *Histoire Naturelle* in which the words *Créateur* or *Dieu* appear a knowledgeable reader has merely to substitute the phrase *puissance de la nature* to arrive at the intended materialistic interpretation.

In effect, the religious passages in the *Histoire Naturelle* are not greatly illuminated by Hérault's confidential asides. The essential point, Buffon's conviction that there are questions to which the intellect of man can never find an answer, is made abundantly clear in the *Histoire Naturelle:* "Causes are and shall forever be unknown to us, for our senses themselves are the effects of causes which we do not know, and they can give us ideas *of effects only,* never of causes" (H.N. I, p. 57). Such views preclude the atheism professed by Hérault, for, among other things, atheism is an affirmation of total confidence in the unaided intellect.

Hérault did not center his study entirely on Buffon's weaknesses, however, though he could hardly be accused of neglecting the negative. He had come to take the measure of a famous writer, or perhaps to learn how one becomes a famous writer, and he found Buffon an indefatigable talker on the subject of literary style, and, in his work habits, an exemplary model.

Buffon confessed that the greatest obstacle he had faced at the beginning of his career was his own constitutional indolence. Certain that for him fame could be won only by hard work, long days of grueling work, the young Buffon had hired a burly peasant to drag him from his bed at 5:00 A.M. each morning and to use whatever force, or violence, was needed to keep him from getting back into bed. In the beginning the peasant earned both tips and bruises in generous measure, but as time passed the full day's work became, Buffon avowed, first a need, and then an ecstasy. For fifty years he followed the same rigid daily schedule during the months he spent at Montbard: up at 5 o'clock in the morning, the routine of dressing and then the first part of the day's work: breakfast (two glasses of wine and a roll) at 9:00 A.M., followed by unbroken work until 2 o'clock in the afternoon; then a long, leisurely dinner with his family and guests, followed by a short nap and a long, solitary walk; back to work at 5:00 P.M. with the final stop at 7:00 P.M.; two hours of relaxing talk in the salon, and, at 9 in the evening, to bed without supper. Never did a naturally indolent man subject himself to a harsher discipline.

This methodical daily routine was matched by equally methodical procedures of composition. Buffon's strongest asset was a phenomenal verbal memory. In the course of his conversations with Hérault he recited verbatim so many lengthy passages from the *Histoire Naturelle,* touching upon whatever subject came to

hand, that Hérault at last became convinced that he knew by
heart the entire massive work, all of the thirty-three volumes then
in print. This powerful memory permitted him to dispense with
all notes at a very early stage of the composition of a particular
article or essay. Rumor had it that, when a youth, he looked too
long at the sun. In any event, his eyesight had been poor almost
from the beginning of his career (Hérault suspected that he was
very nearly blind), and he generally relied upon a small army of
collaborators, assistants, and secretaries to read the necessary
source works to him, or merely to read résumés of the works
which they had made. The few notes he took were normally
burned as soon as he had mastered their contents. He never com-
menced the actual writing of an essay until he had digested all
the relevant material, and the general lines of his own thought
had taken final shape in his mind. Then he dictated the essay
several sentences at a time to a secretary, constantly interrupting
himself to stroll through his hilltop gardens. Hérault was surprised to find, when he was taken on a guided tour of the hilltop
by Buffon's son, that the favorite workroom was not in the smaller
of the two surviving towers, which Buffon liked to refer to in his
letters as his "necromancer's tower," but in a tiny building on the
opposite side of the gardens near the chapel. Ordinarily, the hilltop, which was encircled in descending tiers by a series of iron
fences, was not accessible to visitors until the late afternoon. In
1824, in a conversation with Daniel Webster, Thomas Jefferson
remembered this point with particular clarity:

When I was in France, the Marquis de Chastellux carried me over
to Buffon's residence in the country, and introduced me to him.
It was Buffon's practice to remain in his study till dinner time, and
receive no visitors under any pretense; but his house was open and his
grounds, and a servant showed them very civilly, and invited all stran-
gers and friends to remain to dine. We saw Buffon in the garden, but
carefully avoided him; but we dined with him, and he proved himself
then, as he always did, a man of extraordinary powers in conversation.[6]

When Buffon had finished dictating the first version of an essay,
he would read and correct the secretary's manuscript, usually
emending it drastically, then return it to the secretary to be re-
copied. The second draft, and many succeeding versions, were
similarly corrected until something resembling a final stage

emerged. This was put aside, to be returned to many times in the following days and weeks. Buffon read various versions to friends and visitors, carefully noted their reactions, asked them to paraphrase what they had heard. If any paraphrase differed significantly from the original, further rewritings were undertaken, until every possibility of ambiguity had been eliminated. When Buffon was at last content, the secretary made a final copy, and this was sent to the Imprimerie Royale, to be set up in type under the direction of one of Buffon's associates. The first, second, and even third proofs, as they returned from the Imprimerie, were subjected to the same process as the early manuscripts. When the final version had at length emerged, the manuscripts and proofs relevant to it were customarily burned. Hérault was informed, by one of Buffon's friends, that the celebrated essay *Epoques de la Nature* had passed through seventeen preliminary versions before the final stage was reached. The few preliminary manuscripts that escaped burning, now in the library of the Muséum National d'Histoire Naturelle in Paris, show how painstaking the author's emendations were.

A regimen this strict, writing procedures this arduous, would have struck a chill into the hearts of many young men, but Hérault was not an ordinary young man. He was enchanted with what seemed to be an infallible battle plan for the assault upon the citadel of fame. He was strengthened in his resolve to undertake a project similar to Buffon's *Histoire Naturelle*—apparently something along the lines of the general codification of French law eventually realized under Napoleon. He pressed Buffon for advice, and their interviews quickly took on the character of a literary workshop.

Buffon proved an enthusiastic pedagogue, but he did not make light of the difficulties: "I am still learning, every day, how to write." His insistence on the complexity of stylistic problems drew from Hérault the homage: "No man has better understood the metaphysics of style."

Buffon stressed above all, in these conversations with Hérault, the need for clarity, clarity to be achieved by the judicious use of images—for the intellect cannot function without the aid of the imagination—and comparisons. The abstract must always be tied to the concrete. The most vivid word, not necessarily the most precise word, or *mot propre,* is always to be preferred. The most essential points in the content, the *capita rerum,* must quickly be disengaged from the mass.

Buffon insisted also upon the need to adapt one's style to the subject treated: "I have been obliged to master all possible tones for my work. It is important to know exactly where on the scale one must finish." He insisted no less strenuously on the need for "good faith" on the writer's part. "You can do it," he assured Hérault, vis-à-vis his projected opus, "all that is needed is an upright character and a penetrating and sure intellect."

He warned Hérault against certain aberrations, citing illustrious examples. Jean-Jacques Rousseau, with his abuse of such rhetorical devices as the apostrophe and the interjection, offends against good manners, literary tact. Montesquieu is too choppy, fails to develop his ideas adequately: "I knew him well, and these faults in his style are traceable to certain physical flaws. The *Président* was . . . so excitable that most of the time he couldn't remember what he intended to dictate, so that he had to be content with a very narrow range of ideas."

For once Buffon felt free to unburden himself fully on the subject of his *bête noire*—poetry. Hérault reports, "He did not like poetry. . . . He advised me never to write verse. 'I could have written it, like anyone else,' he told me, 'but I quickly abandoned that genre, in which reason is compelled to go about in chains.'" Somewhat later Buffon added, "Poets cannot be said to have style, because they are tormented by the rules of prosody, before which they are all servile creatures."

Apparently as a kind of final examination, Buffon at last asked his new disciple to try his hand at a critical piece on the *Histoire Naturelle*. Hérault produced a three-hundred-word parallel between the style of Buffon and the style of Rousseau. Buffon's style is likened to, among other things, "a pyramid whose base covers the entire earth and whose summit vanishes into the heavens," a metaphor of dubious purity. Buffon was, nevertheless, delighted. He spent five days rewriting the three hundred words and then suggested that Hérault publish it in one of the Paris reviews, perhaps the *Mercure.*

By the end of the visit a strong affection had been established between the young man and the old. In the last pages of his book Hérault de Séchelles referred to Buffon as "my new father." And Buffon permitted himself a rather personal comment, in the nature of expert public relations advice: " 'You have two names,' he told me; 'people refer to you sometimes by one, sometimes by the other, and sometimes by both together. Believe me, use just one; we must never let the public become confused.' "

CHAPTER 3

Youth

I *Metamorphosis*

IN a brief biographical memoir prepared shortly after Buffon's death for the use of the official eulogists, the Chevalier de Buffon, the much younger half-brother of the author of the *Histoire Naturelle,* stated that Buffon's career as a student had been marked by "no pronounced superiority" and that "one can cite of his childhood, and even of his adolescence, only those traits which are common to all children graced with some degree of native wit." [1] The Marquis de Bois-St-Just, who claimed to have been well acquainted with Buffon in his last years, affirmed, in his *Paris, Versailles et les provinces au XVIIIe siècle,* that "M. de Buffon was regarded at the *collège* as a youth of markedly inferior abilities." [2] In December 1733, when Buffon, at the age of twenty-six, first entered the Académie des Sciences, the Abbé Le Blanc, certainly one of Buffon's closest friends at that time, remarked in a letter, "I have long been predicting that he [Buffon] would give evidence one day of a good head." [3] The few surviving letters written by Buffon in his youth lend support to the suggestion that he was then, to all appearances, a very ordinary young man.

The changes, the metamorphoses, that made him one of the most impressive figures of his age would seem to have taken place in the course of the Grand Tour he took in the years 1730–32 through France and Italy in the company of two Englishmen. The changes involved even his name, for it was toward the end of the tour that he began to add *de Buffon* to his signature *Leclerc.* It was only after 1734 that he shortened the signature to *Buffon.*

Georges-Louis Leclerc, the future Buffon, was born in Montbard in 1707. His father, Benjamin-François Leclerc, was a minor civil servant, administrator of the salt tax, the *gabelle,* in the town. In 1714, Buffon's maternal uncle, a *fermier général* for the

king of Sicily, died, leaving an immense fortune to Buffon's
mother, and the constricted career of Benjamin-François Leclerc
entered a new phase. He promptly purchased the lands and village of Buffon, just outside of Montbard, the castellanship of
Montbard itself, a pretentious townhouse in Dijon, the provincial
capital, and an appointment as *conseiller* in the Parlement of
Dijon. From this time the family resided principally in Dijon,
and Buffon attended the Jesuit Collège des Godrans in that city.
He received the *baccalauréat* in 1725, at the age of seventeen, the
licence from the Faculté de Dijon in 1726, at the age of eighteen,
and successfully passed examinations in the law on July 17, 1726.
Little definite is known of the next few years. He passed some
time in Angers, apparently studying medicine and botany. He
began also to study mathematics quite intensively, carrying on a
correspondence with such brilliant young mathematicians as Gabriel Cramer and Alexis Clairaut.[4]

In a letter he wrote from Nantes on November 5, 1730, we find
him already embarked on his Grand Tour. There are no extant
documents showing precisely when the tour began or how and
when he met his two English companions, Dr. Nathan Hickman
and the second Duke of Kingston, Hickman's pupil. Hickman's
account books, which are among the papers of the Kingston family
deposited at the present time in the manuscript collection of the
University of Nottingham, indicate that Kingston and Hickman
resided in Dijon (after a brief stop in Montbard) at least from
March 7, 1729, to August 6, 1729, and in Angers from August 24,
1729, to January 15, 1730, and it was in all probability during this
period that they became acquainted with Buffon.[5]

II *The Grand Tour*

There is much to indicate that Buffon's character, or at least his
personality, changed significantly during his Grand Tour. What
little is known of his two companions does not add greatly to our
understanding of these changes, and the few surviving letters of
Buffon that bear on the tour are not much more helpful. These
letters are for the most part addressed to Gilles-Germain Richard
de Ruffey, a classmate at the Collège des Godrans and a lifelong
friend.

In his letter to Ruffey from Nantes in November, 1730, we find
Buffon resolved to continue his journey despite the "vindictive

fury" of a persistent fever. A provincial Burgundian, he evidently regarded the people of Nantes as a species of foreigners, and he found them greedy and boorish, but he tolerantly concluded that their unpretentiously bourgeois mode of life was more "rational" than the insufferable affectation of the petty *noblesse de robe* of Dijon. Three months later, January 22, 1731, he wrote to Ruffey from Bordeaux. He was still suffering from the fever, "become a veritable Proteus for me, attacking me under a thousand different forms," and "leaving me only skin and bones and scarcely enough strength to drag them about." He had found the people of Bordeaux, in general, an amalgam of fops and boors, the streets quagmires, and the gambling decidedly amateurish.

On April 2, 1731, he wrote to Ruffey from Montpellier. Spring had come early in the Midi and the nagging fevers of winter were already distant memories. He had passed a month at Montauban, visited Toulouse, Carcassonne, Béziers, and Narbonne, before settling at Montpellier, and his observations of the natives, now expanded to include ladies and *savants* as well as merchants and gamblers, sparkle with new enthusiasm: "The female population of Toulouse is wonderfully handsome; the very old excepted, I cannot recall having seen a single ugly woman in that city." And, for the first time in a letter to Ruffey, the presence of the Duke of Kingston is noted, with an allusion to "magnificent lodgings. Milord pays fifty livres a month." It is probably to the incredible luxury in which Kingston traveled that we must look for an answer to his influence upon Buffon. For many months Buffon was an honored guest in a perambulating ducal establishment that involved a number of coaches and a host of permanent servants. Whatever else he might have been, Kingston was an authentic grandee, an intoxicating model for a young provincial to study.

In late July, 1731, Buffon was again in Dijon, called home by "family affairs," doubtless the final illness of his mother who died on August 1, 1731. He probably rejoined Kingston and Hickman in Lyons, where they made a lengthy stay, before setting out for Geneva. The party entered Italy by way of "the thrilling passage over Mount Cenis," in the phrase of Joseph Spence, who had traveled with them for a brief period. Spence does not seem to have taken any notice of Buffon, as in his description of the Mount Cenis passage:

Over night one of the prime ministers of the King of Sardinia for that village came to take measure of us . . . to view each person and see how many men would be necessary to carry him up the hill. Lord Middlesex [Spence's pupil] had four assigned him, the Duke of Kingston six, and his governor, who is a portly, plump gentleman, no less than eight.[6]

On January 20, 1732, Buffon wrote to Ruffey from Rome, presenting a lively account of the Eternal City:

Rome is at this hour in all its glory; the carnival began two weeks ago; four magnificent operas and as many comedies, this without counting the minor theaters, are here "ordinary" pleasures, and I admit that for me they are most extraordinary, by the excellence of the music, the wild frivolity of the dances, the brilliance of the décor. . . .

All solid documentation relating to Buffon's Grand Tour ends at this point, in the winter of 1732. In August he was in Paris for his first long period of residence in that city. To the best of our knowledge, he never again undertook a trip of any length, aside from his annual circuits, as regular as the seasons, between Paris and Montbard. The most celebrated theoretical biologist and geologist of the eighteenth century was one of its least traveled writers.

Kingston and Hickman arrived in Paris, probably at about the same time as Buffon, to reside there more or less continuously until December, 1736, when the young duke returned to England, "abducting" in the process a married Frenchwoman, his mistress Mme de La Touche. Buffon, still an intimate friend of the two Englishmen, persuaded M. de La Touche, very possibly by methods verging on blackmail, to abandon his projected legal proceedings against Kingston.

III *Two Doubtful Sources*

The record of these early years of Buffon's life has been considerably clouded by two rather dubious documents: the first, a biographical memoir prepared by the Capuchin monk Ignace Bougot, chaplain of Buffon's estates in the little village of Buffon and, in form at least, the spiritual advisor of the author of the *Histoire Naturelle* in the last years of his life, and, the second, a

newspaper obituary notice written by a M. Godard, a friend of
Ignace's, that appeared in the *Journal de Paris* in May, 1788.[7]
Godard's article, because of its early appearance, several weeks
after Buffon's death, served as a prime source both for the articles
on Buffon in the various biographical dictionaries and also for the
eulogies of Buffon in the months following his death, including
that delivered by Condorcet in the Académie des Sciences. Ignace's
memoir, on the other hand, although long in the possession
of Nadault de Buffon, was not published until 1885, in the second
edition of Nadault's *Correspondance de Buffon*. There are statements in Godard's article, however, which suggest that Ignace
furnished much of the information Godard presents, and there
are a number of points of information that are advanced only by
Godard and Ignace. These points are not supported by the more
authoritative memoirs prepared by Buffon's intimates, such as that
written by Buffon's brother, the Chevalier de Buffon, with the aid
of Buffon's son, which Nadault published in both the first and the
second edition of the *Correspondance*. Moreover, Ignace's memoir
is inaccurate on a number of factual points that can easily be
checked, and, at times, it is obviously fanciful, and even absurdly
extravagant.

Ignace was a bizarre figure, almost, according to Hérault de
Séchelles' account of him, a sort of court jester in Buffon's retinue:

M. de Buffon has referred to him [Ignace] as his friend in the article
on the canary. He is also his lackey: I have seen him following M. de
Buffon on his walks, awkwardly hobbling immediately behind him, for
he is quite lame, the whole forming a tableau to challenge the art of
the printmaker, the author of the *Histoire Naturelle* marching proudly,
his head high, a man apart, scarcely deigning to glance upon the
earth that bears him, absorbed in his thoughts, resembling "Man" as
depicted in his history of man, a portrait doubtless modeled upon himself, holding in his right hand a walking stick, his other hand majestically propped upon his left hip.

I have seen him [Ignace], when the valets were absent, remove his
master's napkin, and the little table as well upon which he had just
dined. Buffon would respond: "I thank you, my dear child." And Ignace, assuming a humble attitude, had more the air of a domestic
servant than the very servants themselves.

This same Ignace, Capuchin-lackey, is in addition the lackey-
confessor of M. de Buffon.

Hérault extended his comic touches even to the physical description he gave of Ignace:

If you wish to form some idea of his person you must picture a fat fellow with a round head, exactly resembling a mask of the Harlequin of the Comédie Italienne, and this comparison appears to me so much the more just because he speaks precisely in the manner of Carlin: the same accent, the same wheedling tone.[8]

It is far less difficult to believe that Buffon amused himself by telling this simple and apparently boundlessly credulous man tall tales about his youth than it is to believe everything that Ignace reports. Simply believing in Ignace's existence is sufficiently difficult.

Nevertheless, several of Ignace's "facts" gained wide currency. It was apparently on the sole authority of Ignace's memoir that Nadault de Buffon stated in his *Correspondance* that Buffon had fought three violent and bloody duels in his youth.[9] Similarly, the story that Buffon made a lengthy and colorful sojourn in England as the guest of the Duke of Kingston, an event that does not fit into the pattern of Buffon's movements that can be established on the basis of the now available extant correspondence (much of it unknown to Nadault), also appears to rest on the unsupported testimony of Ignace and Godard alone.[10]

Unfortunately, such stories, though they may be patently out of character or even well nigh physically impossible, cannot be rejected outright. It is virtually impossible to prove that something did not happen. To quote Buffon himself: "It is well known that in the matter of testimony by witnesses the assertion of two positive witnesses to the effect that they have seen something constitutes completely acceptable proof, whereas the testimony of a thousand or ten thousand negative witnesses, who merely assert that they have not seen something, suffices only to produce a slight doubt" (H.N. I, pp. 294–95). Even if substantial new documentation should be unearthed, it is unlikely that accounts of Buffon's youth will ever be completely free of the elements of confusion introduced by Ignace and Godard.

IV *A Fortune Secured and Enlarged*

The sudden maturing of Buffon's character following his association with Kingston and Hickman is most noticeable in his
letters to his friend Ruffey. The tone of the letters that antedate
the Grand Tour is in general querulous and plaintive, decidedly
adolescent, as in the following, written in 1729 when Buffon was
twenty-two:

As for me, I shall do whatever lies in my power to keep myself away
from Dijon as long as I can, and if there is anything at all that can
bring me back there with pleasure, that can only be the desire I feel
to see again the very small number of those for whom I retain some
feelings of esteem.

In the letters written in 1732 the tone has become self-reliant,
coldly determined, confident, ambitious—the familiar tone of the
mature Buffon. The following was addressed to Ruffey from the
vicinity of Montbard on October 25, 1732, and describes the crisis
that had cut short Buffon's first period of residence in Paris following the completion of the Grand Tour:

You could certainly, sir, never divine what is holding me here, nor
could you suspect that my father, at the age of fifty, could show himself sufficiently enamored, or, to put the matter plainly, sufficiently
mad to give me cause to fear a second marriage, and that with a girl
of twenty-two, who, aside from her youth, has almost nothing in her
favor. You perceive, sir, the great wrong that this affair would do me;
thus you may judge of the force with which I oppose it. As I have some
expectations of success, I must beg you to keep this matter secret . . .
the situation in which I find myself is not without similarity to that in
which I have ofttimes seen you; I speak of the discontent of a well-born
son occasioned by an obdurate or passionate parent.

Buffon did not succeed in preventing the marriage of his "obdurate or passionate parent." The marriage took place in Montbard
on December 30, 1732. In January Buffon arrived in Dijon, loudly
proclaiming his intention of instituting legal proceedings against
his father for the recovery of his personal share of his mother's
fortune. He was without allies. Of the five offspring of the first
marriage of Benjamin-François Leclerc, only Buffon, the eldest,

remained to dispute his father's trusteeship. A son, Jean-Marc, at the age of twenty-two, and a daughter, Anne-Madeleine, at the age of twenty, had both died in 1731; of the remaining children, Charles-Benjamin had become a Cistercian monk and Jeanne an Ursuline nun. Buffon evidently had little need of allies however, for his father was compelled, presumably without formal proceedings, to agree to a handsome settlement. Buffon acquired full title to a fortune of 80,000 livres, as well as the house and the lands of the Leclercs in Montbard. Moreover, the nearby village of Buffon, which had been sold, was repurchased, though not with an entirely clear title, and ceded to him, a very necessary detail inasmuch as he had already added the name of these none-too-valuable estates, and *la particule*, to his plebeian patronymic. The settlement was not without ill-feeling. A third of a century later Buffon and his father still communicated through intermediaries,[11] although Buffon's relations with the two offspring of this second marriage of his father's, Mme Nadault and the Chevalier de Buffon, were always close.

His titles secure, the young Buffon immediately began the remodeling and landscaping of his new properties, and he launched himself into a series of commercial ventures in his native Burgundy that would in time enormously augment his personal fortune.

His first enterprise was a tree nursery, designed to furnish young trees to the provincial government for planting along the roads of Burgundy. He established the nursery at Montbard in 1734 and, by careful management, brought it to a value of 1,500 livres by 1736, at which time he sold it to the government for 2,500 livres, with the additional understanding that he himself would be engaged, at a handsome salary, as "administrator" of the new government nursery. Those who have examined the still-surviving accounts of this nursery in the Archives of the Côte-d'Or have satisfied themselves that Buffon acquitted himself well in this post and that the state profited to at least as great an extent as Buffon himself.[12]

This early transaction has all the salient features of the later transactions, such as the iron foundry he established in the village of Buffon, and can serve as a sort of paradigm of Buffon's business procedures. Buffon had already acquired powerful friends in high places, possibly meeting many at Kingston's parties in Paris, and he made full use, without hesitation and without nagging scruples, of his ministerial backing. In Buffon's case, however, this does not necessarily imply corruption. His account books are extant and they bear inspection. His personal profits were immense, but so too were the public benefits involved. There was, as it were, a virtual identification of private and public interests.

The scale of his business operations is suggested by a description of the foundry he established in the village of Buffon, written by his secretary Humbert-Bazile:

I have seen in M. de Buffon's ironworks seven tilt hammers in action at one time; in those days they manufactured there every variety of iron, rods, sheet iron, steel, etc. The main building has an impressive façade; a double stairway leads to the area opposite the blast furnace; there are lofty porticoes on both sides, one leading to the furnaces and the other to the bellows. The main gear wheel is fifty feet in diameter; buckets attached to a paddle wheel raise the water needed to sprinkle the spacious gardens that decorate the approaches to the foundry. At the rear of the main courtyard there is a chapel in which the Abbé Mignot, a parish priest of Montbard, came to celebrate mass every Sunday. There are alcoves on both sides of the porch leading from the great staircase to the furnace, and the appearance of this truly monumental entranceway is so majestic that, at the time it was being constructed, the country people used to doff their hats in passing, believing it to be an edifice consecrated to the faith.[13]

A few remnants of these structures still stand and are in use as farm sheds, though (on one particular summer day in 1966, at any rate) access to them is apt to be barred by very large, unfriendly dogs. At its peak this singularly ornate rural industrial plant and research center, that has since been reabsorbed so completely into the surrounding countryside, furnished employment for as many as four hundred workers at a time.[14] It represented a total investment of almost half a million livres on Buffon's part.[15] Cannon for both the army and the navy were manufactured there, as well as the iron fences for the Jardin du Roi, some of which are still in place along the Rue de Buffon in Paris.[16] Léon Bertin, in his article *"Buffon, Homme d'Affaires"* remarks: "As proprietor of an ironworks, Buffon assumed a role, in the middle of the eighteenth century, fully comparable to that of a great industrialist of the nineteenth or even of the twentieth century. His plant was the most respected in the kingdom." [17]

An excerpt from a still unpublished letter of September 7, 1785, now in the manuscript collection of the library of the Muséum d'Histoire Naturelle in Paris, addressed to André Thouin, an official of the Jardin du Roi who acted as Buffon's principal agent in the purchase of land for the expansion of the Jardin, affords some insights into Buffon's imaginative business ethics:

I have already indicated to you that you need not bear the expense for the enclosure of your little piece of land. I request, therefore, that you carry on your statement [in the account books of the Jardin du Roi] for the first biweekly period, or the following, all that you have paid out for it, because I intend that the piece of land that now belongs to me will one day belong to the King and, consequently, it is permissible for me, at the present time, to carry on the books the cost of the enclosure on the side that borders my piece of land.[18]

Because of the long delays involved in obtaining money from his superiors, Buffon regularly advanced, out of his own pocket, the money for the operating expenses of the Jardin du Roi, often making sizable purchases first in his own name and afterward reselling (at a profit) to the government. As might be expected, this procedure sometimes gave rise to eccentricities in bookkeeping that would profoundly shock a modern governmental investigating commission, but the procedures were in accord with the usages of the time, and Buffon, a dedicated if not disinterested public servant, was the eventual loser, for reimbursement became more and more difficult to obtain, and, at his death in 1788, the almost bankrupt government owed him 200,000 livres, a sum never repaid.[19]

Despite occasional lapses, however, Buffon was an astonishingly successful businessman, particularly so in view of the fact that he devoted so little time to his commercial affairs. His various business ventures assured him, at the height of his career, an annual income of 80,000 livres. The importance of this sum can best be judged by some observations made by Buffon in his *Essai d'arithmétique morale* (H.N.S. IV, p. 77, note d):

The minimum annual income needed by a king would be, for example, ten million livres (because a king who had less would be a poor king); the income absolutely necessary to a gentleman, a man of condition, would be ten thousand livres (because a gentleman with less would be an impoverished *seigneur*); the income needed by a peasant would be five hundred livres, because, unless he lived in abject squalor, he could not spend less and clothe and nourish his family.

Buffon's income was thus eight times that needed to maintain an aristocratic train of life under the *ancien régime,* a very handsome margin.

CHAPTER 4

Rise to Fame

I *Scientific Debut*

A letter Buffon wrote to his old friend Ruffey from Paris in August, 1732, closes with instructions to post future letters to him "at the residence of M. Boulduc, the King's Apothecary." Gilles-François Boulduc was a chemist of considerable note, a figure of importance at Versailles, at the Académie des Sciences, and, most significantly, at the Jardin du Roi. At this time, his work on soluble salts found in the soil was attracting much attention, notably that of the young but already famous agronomist and chemist Henri-Louis Duhamel du Monceau.

Now, although Buffon's name first appeared in the *Mémoires* of the Académie des Sciences in 1733 [1] in connection with his ingenious solutions of several mathematical problems—described with more enthusiasm than lucidity by the aging Fontenelle, the academy's "perpetual secretary"—his first serious scientific venture was a series of silviculture experiments carried out under government auspices in partnership with Duhamel du Monceau. Duhamel had been chosen in 1731 to direct this series of experiments, through which the minister Maurepas, later Buffon's chief patron, hoped to promote reforestation on a national scale and to develop a better quality of wood for the ships of the French navy. Buffon's experiments, conducted on his estates in Burgundy, with their extensive holdings in timberland, were begun in the spring of 1733, at first independently and then for a time in collaboration with Duhamel. He was still presenting reports of his results in the publications of the Académie des Sciences in 1744, reports later reprinted for the most part in the volumes of *Suppléments* of the *Histoire Naturelle* (H.N.S. II). The commercial tree nursery venture of 1734 was one offshoot of these activities, as was also the ambitious landscaping of the hill behind his villa.

It is curious to find Buffon, later the most reckless of theoreticians, beginning his scientific career in the ranks of the cautious experimenters, enemies of all theory, and in an applied, not a pure science. To identify the causative factors involved in the irregular growth patterns of trees, he measured dozens of trees, amassing his results in formidable tables. He checked out the idea that a stronger wood could be produced by stripping the bark off a living tree and permitting it to dry out before it was cut, tirelessly rechecking, setting up all possible varieties of the experiment: completely stripped trees, partially stripped trees, fruit trees, oaks, isolated trees, trees protected by brush, trees in the depths of his forests, and so on. He devised an ingenious apparatus to measure the strength of wood (i.e., the quantity of weights necessary to bend and break it), taking into account all conceivable varieties in the texture of the wood. One data table follows another in dizzying array in these early reports.

He modeled his work on that of the great English botanical experimenter Stephen Hales, translating Hales's most important published work into French in 1735 and presenting it with an introduction of his own. But Buffon very quickly revealed himself as a decidedly heterodox Baconian, and this was probably the cause of his early break with his first collaborator, the resolutely conservative Duhamel du Monceau. He gave to his conclusions on the effects of winter cold snaps on the growth of trees a theoretical breadth that no true Baconian could tolerate, suggesting already his later theorizing in the *Histoire Naturelle* on heat as the essential principle of life. His thoughts on ecology, particularly on the harmful effects of completely uncontrolled forest growth, also presage passages in the *Histoire Naturelle*. He resolved the difficulty presented by the extremely variant figures he obtained in his experiments on wood strength by offering generalized figures, which he called *"réelles,"* but which were in fact the product of pure conjecture. In the last reports of the long series, the method of organization has undergone a significant change: the endless tables are suppressed, tersely summarized, and the conclusions are presented first, not last. The conclusions had become theories, suggestive of the great systems to come; they were no longer, as in the beginning, simply minimal generalizations dictated by the data.[2]

Above all, this early work was Buffonian in its gigantic scope. It somehow had the dramatic quality Buffon managed to infuse into everything he did, as his friend the Abbé Le Blanc vividly suggested in a personal tribute in his book *Les Lettres d'un Français:*

Your penetrating genius has made you discover very early what others learn only by experience; and you have had from your infancy a taste for what is commonly the fruits of old age. For who besides yourself ever thought of planting trees at eighteen years of age? For even in England, where they have tried every thing, attempted every thing; has any one had the courage to set apart an hundred acres of his land, to make experiments on trees? They pretend that Solomon, who was acquainted with every plant and tree, from the *hyssop* to the *cedar*, wrote a book on the manner of cultivating trees and plants, which we have lost: tell the truth, sir, did you not find it? If not, nobody since so many ages, has been more capable of repairing that loss. You will do great service, not only to our nation, but to mankind in general. . . .[3]

It is typical of Buffon too that he did not confine himself entirely to one field of inquiry during these early years of scientific activity in the 1730's. Although silviculture was definitely his specialty at this time, he reported experiments to the Académie des Sciences in a wide range of other areas: gravitational pull, pendulum movements, ballistics, rocketry, optical phenomena, and even zoology. He continued his work in mathematics, submitting to the academy his solutions to several knotty problems.

Toward the end of the decade he began work on a translation of an early essay of Newton's on calculus, which he published in 1740. He was an indifferent Baconian, but a fanatical Newtonian. Voltaire, a prominent figure in the struggle to supplant Cartesian with Newtonian physics in France, found this zeal discomfiting. On October 3, 1739, he permitted himself some heavy irony on the subject in a letter to Helvétius, then Buffon's guest at Montbard and a close friend of both men:

My young Apollo, I received your charming letter. If I were not with Mme du Châtelet I should wish to be at Montbard. I don't know quite how I shall go about sending a short and modest reply that I have made to the anti-Newtonians. I am the abandoned child of a movement of which M. de Buffon is the chief, and I am rather like those soldiers who fight with enthusiasm without any very clear understanding of the interests of their prince.[4]

In another letter to Helvétius, of October 27, 1740, Voltaire gives us the best and most succinct vignette we have of Buffon at this period:

Aren't you at present with M. de Buffon? That fellow is moving . . . toward glory . . . but he is also moving toward happiness. He is wonderfully healthy. The body of an athlete and the soul of a sage, that's what one needs to be happy.[5]

II *The Career Takes Wing*

Buffon entered the Académie des Sciences as an *adjoint* in the *Section de Mécanique* in January, 1734, moved to the *Section de Botanique,* still as *adjoint,* in March, 1739, and, in June, 1739, he at last achieved the rank of *membre associé* in the botanical section. At the age of thirty-one, after a slow start, he had made his way into the first ranks of France's men of science. His reputation was solid, based on experiments that still stand scrutiny, and his colleagues had learned to expect from him flashes of brilliance, or even, some suspected, of genius.

On July 16, 1739, Charles-François de Cisternay Dufay, superintendent of the Jardin du Roi since 1732, died suddenly in Paris. He had been an exceptional administrator, and under his leadership the Jardin, long a neglected institution, had begun to acquire its international reputation as a research center. Duhamel du Monceau, Buffon's senior partner at the beginning of the silviculture experiments, was generally regarded as the logical successor to Dufay. But Duhamel was absent, in England, at the time. Buffon's patrons, the academician Jean Hellot and the minister Maurepas, acted at once to secure the post for Buffon. It was alleged that Dufay himself, before his death, had singled out Buffon as his successor. The king was suitably impressed, and Buffon became the new superintendent. Upon his belated return from England, Duhamel was compensated for his loss with an appointment as Inspector General of the Navy.

Buffon plunged immediately into the arduous duties of his new post. Throughout the forty-nine years that he was to hold the position of superintendent, a major segment of his energy would be devoted to pushing to completion the work begun by Dufay. The establishment included at this period public lectureships in botany, chemistry and anatomy, extensive botanical gardens, and the Cabinet du Roi, a heterogeneous natural-history collection. Dufay had renovated the more dilapidated buildings, constructed a new amphitheater for the lectures, and expanded the botanical gardens, building many new greenhouses. Buffon turned his attention first to the natural history collection, which he found in deplorable condition. He continued Dufay's building program, to furnish needed space for the collection, and, on his own authority, instituted a policy of purchasing adjacent lands, which, in his time, approximately doubled the area occupied by the Jardin. The present-day establishment on this site, which includes the Paris zoo, botanical gardens, and natural history museums and libraries, was to a considerable extent the creation of Buffon.[6]

Dufay had established a modest network of business contacts and correspondents whose principal purpose was to facilitate the purchase and transportation of specimens for the Jardin. Buffon soon perceived the advantage of expanding Dufay's system and of placing it on a less informal and a less purely commercial basis. With the support of the minister Maurepas he was able to establish a *Brevet de Correspondant du Jardin du Roi et du Cabinet d'Histoire Naturelle,* with the understanding that the official positions associated with these certificates were to be largely honorary and would not noticeably increase the expenses of the Jardin. Buffon soon added to his duties the project of publishing a descriptive catalogue of the reorganized and enlarged Cabinet du Roi, and this proposed catalogue quickly developed into his monumental *Histoire Naturelle.* The network of *correspondants* then became useful primarily as a source of information, rather than of specimens alone.

A number of circumstances favored the almost unlimited expansion of the network of correspondents. It has often been remarked that throughout Europe the cultivated amateur, the *honnête homme,* of the eighteenth century often took an all but professional interest in the progress of the sciences. A number of the most significant discoveries of the age were made by men who were essentially amateurs. Daniel Mornet, in his *Les Sciences de la nature en France au XVIII⁰ siècle,* has credited Buffon with giving to the *gens du monde* who showed some interest in natural history *"l'illusion de pénétrer dans le Temple même."* [7] The almost immediate popular success achieved by the *Histoire Naturelle* when the first volumes appeared in 1749 had made it a

signal honor, and one much sought after, to have one's name cited
in the pages of that illustrious and quite possibly immortal work.
Even the Comte de Maurepas, Buffon's patron, was not averse to
seeing it noted specifically that the extraordinary carp mentioned
in the second volume, "whose age can be authenticated at well
over one hundred and fifty years and who yet appeared to me to
be as agile and as lively as ordinary carp," were to be found "in
the moats of M. le Comte de Maurepas' château of Pontchartrain"
(H.N. II, p. 309). Among Buffon's correspondents were the kings
of Denmark, Poland, Sweden, and Prussia, Catherine the Great
of Russia, two first ministers of England (Pitt and Bute), Benjamin Franklin, and Thomas Jefferson. The most useful of Buffon's
correspondents, those who could be trusted never to waste his
time, were French colonial civil servants and explorers, and, of
course, the professional men of science, his colleagues in the
various learned societies to which he belonged.

His elections to eminent academies included the Royal Society
of London (1740), the Academy of Dijon (1740), the Philosophical Society of Edinburgh (1745), the Academy of Berlin (1746),
the Académie Française (1753), the Philosophical Society of
Philadelphia (1768), the Imperial Academy of Saint Petersburg
(1777), and the American Academy of Arts and Sciences of Boston (1782). The most novel of these distinctions was, like his
election to the Académie Française, literary in nature; in 1777,
almost a septuagenarian, he was voted membership "by solemn
acclamation" in the Arcadian Academy of Rome, and this august
and poetical body then conferred upon him the honorary quality
of Arcadian Shepherd and a suitably romantic name, Archytas of
Thessaly.

The personal fame that made it possible for Buffon to establish
a network of informants extending to every accessible point on
the surface of the earth and to enjoy membership in every notable
learned society was chiefly founded on the popularity of the
Histoire Naturelle. In 1910 Professor Mornet examined five hundred published catalogues of private libraries sold in Paris between 1750 and 1780 and established a list of the works most commonly owned. Pierre Bayle's Dictionnaire led the list and Buffon's
Histoire Naturelle was in third place.[8] But Buffon's fame was also
due in part to his remarkable public relations sense. He had
reached the height of fame very early in his career, in 1747, prior

to the publication of the first volumes of the *Histoire Naturelle,*
on the strength of a single experiment, artfully chosen for its
dramatic possibilities.

To disprove Descartes' theoretical demonstration of the impossibility of constructing a burning lens or mirror capable of setting
fires at a considerable distance by concentrating the sun's rays
on a target area, the device which Archimedes was said to have
used against the Roman fleet at Syracuse, Buffon set out to construct such a machine, and succeeded. After a number of failures,
he hit upon the device of an upright wooden grid on which a
large number of small, flat mirrors were attached by adjustable
screws that permitted each individual mirror to be aimed by
hand, and with this device he was able to ignite wood at a distance of more than two hundred feet. The spectacle of a modern
scientist recreating one of the fabled marvels of antiquity, in
defiance of a theoretical pronouncement by the great Descartes
himself, stirred imaginations across all of Europe. Spectators
flocked to the demonstrations, and even King Louis XV con-
descended to view the new marvel in operation. Frederick the
Great of Prussia sent the hitherto little known French physicist
his personal congratulations. Buffon had made his name, the name
he had chosen for its simplicity and euphony, for the ease with
which it could be remembered, a household word throughout
Europe.

III *Le Chef d'Equipe*

Buffon's success in his many areas of endeavor—as the administrator of a scientific institute, as an academician, as a businessman,
and as an author, both popular and scholarly—owed much to his
qualities of personal leadership. He had the gift of winning loyalty
from younger men of great ability, loyalty that was not shaken
even when he took full credit for the success of joint efforts. He
seemed always to be able to find clever and industrious men
willing to assume part of his burden, and to work in his shadow.
A complete list of the members of Buffon's "team" through the
years would include more than a dozen names; the most important of these men were Louis Daubenton, Philibert Gueneau de
Montbeillard, the Abbé Bexon, Edme Daubenton, and André
Thouin.

At first the tasks of directing the Jardin and composing the

Histoire Naturelle were not clearly distinguished, and the country doctor Louis Daubenton, Buffon's first collaborator on the *Histoire Naturelle,* author of the detailed anatomical studies that appeared in the early volumes, was also one of Buffon's most important assistants at the Jardin. Daubenton was, like Buffon, a native of Montbard, and his family had long and close ties with Buffon's family. He withdrew from active collaboration on the *Histoire Naturelle* in 1767 after Buffon obtained total financial control of the venture, becoming in effect his own publisher, and moved to limit the scope of the anatomical articles, which he felt were discouraging sales, but Daubenton remained a prominent figure at the Jardin and his personal and professional relations with Buffon remained cordial. His opinions on particular questions are often cited in later volumes of the *Histoire Naturelle.*

The two men who succeeded Daubenton as Buffon's leading collaborators on the *Histoire Naturelle* were not attached to the Jardin, and the two tasks thus became more distinct. Philibert Gueneau de Montbeillard, a country gentleman of the Burgundian town of Samur, a short ride from Montbard, was, like Daubenton, an old friend and neighbor younger than Buffon by approximately a decade; he was an enthusiastic amateur of the sciences and had contributed articles to Diderot's *Encyclopédie,* but sheer arrogance, to judge from a biographical sketch left by his wife, and an unfortunate tendency toward nervous breakdowns prevented him from seeking a permanent position of any nature and bound him to his estates.[9] The Abbé Gabriel Bexon, some forty years younger than Buffon, tiny, frail and hunchbacked, who struggled desperately throughout his brief and blighted life to support a mother and a sister with his writing, received small cash payments and a clerical sinecure for his substantial contributions to the *Histoire Naturelle.*[10] Buffon's relationship with Bexon represented his one really intimate contact with genuine human misery over a period of years, and his letters to the chronically ill abbé, though largely devoted to details of the collaboration, are among the very few in which he occasionally dropped his habitual formal tone and attempted, clumsily, to display warmth and affection: "Be sure to follow my divisions and my method for the parrots. . . . I divide them first into two large classes: those of the Old World and those of the New World . . . but, above all, my very dear Abbé, do not hurry yourself; take care of your little guts." [11]

The contributions of Gueneau de Montbeillard (which were limited largely to the *Histoire Naturelle des Oiseaux*) and those of the Abbé Bexon (which began in the later volumes of the *Histoire Naturelle des Oiseaux* and extended into the *Suppléments* and the *Histoire Naturelle des Minéraux*) were, unlike those of Daubenton, not clearly demarcated from those of Buffon himself. Both men wrote in styles that were substantially pastiches of Buffon's, and, as Buffon's acknowledgments of their efforts were somewhat casual, it is often very difficult to establish the authorship of many articles in these sections of the *Histoire Naturelle*. Buffon's practice was always to attempt to turn everything to his own advantage, and he apparently saw no reason why, if a great and successful writer in the course of a long career inspires a host of younger imitators, he should not draw some profit from the ablest among them. He was highly pleased with the result. His letters to Gueneau de Montbeillard in particular contain much praise for that touchy aristocrat's pseudo-Buffonian style: "I enjoyed your [piece on the] ortolans as much as if I had eaten them." [12] Purists among his admirers, however, like the archbluestocking Mme Necker, were sometimes less pleased, perhaps scenting a challenge to the impeccability of their literary taste. "Gueneau de Montbeillard's pen of steel," Mme Necker remarked, "could never perfectly imitate the traces of M. de Buffon's soft brush; his writing was overly emphatic." [13]

Barthélemy de Faujas de Saint-Fond, the distinguished geologist and pioneer balloonist to whom Buffon had intended to pass on the task of completing the *Histoire Naturelle*, and the Count de Lacépède, called "the king of the serpents," the youthful official of the Jardin du Roi who usurped and actually accomplished that task, must also be named among the more prominent members of the team that enabled Buffon to make of the *Histoire Naturelle*, among other things, a reputable reference work which, with major revisions, would remain in use for almost a century after his death. Buffon's main legacy was the unfinished task he left, and the chance for fame and glory it promised. And so the abrupt displacement of Faujas, his "official" but dilatory successor, by the ambitious and unscrupulous Count de Lacépède, was a subject for much indignation on the part of Faujas himself as well as many of Buffon's closest intimates. Still it is highly probable that Buffon would have looked with at least as much

favor on the resourceful Lacépède as on the heroic and righteous
Faujas.

There were also a few minor figures on the "team." Edme Daubenton, known as "Daubenton le jeune," was a cousin of Louis
Daubenton's. He served at the Jardin as *sous-démonstrateur du
Cabinet du Roi,* and he was charged with the direction of the
artists who prepared the illustrative plates for the *Histoire Naturelle* in addition to his duties at the Jardin. André Thouin was,
from 1764 at the age of seventeen, *jardinier en chef* of the Jardin
du Roi. During the greater part of each year, when Buffon was
absent in Montbard, Thouin actually functioned as director of
the establishment, receiving Buffon's instructions by mail from
time to time.

Buffon's letters to Thouin are testimonials to his concern for
minute detail, ranging from security precautions (with Buffon, of
course, as master sleuth) to the protocol involved in discharging
obligations with miniature portraits of Buffon mounted on snuff-
boxes: "I see, my very dear M. Thouin, by the account you have
given me of the theft of our shrubs and of the steps you have
taken in consequence, I see, I repeat, that this theft can only
have been accomplished by a man familiar with the routines of
the Jardin du Roi and that there is also ample reason to believe
that this man is the very same who committed the first theft and
whom you chased. . . ." [14] "With respect to the little presents,
I should think myself less than generous, after all of the efforts
that M. Guillemin has made, and will continue to make, if I
offered him a box worth no more than ten louis; it will be necessary, my dear M. Thouin, to have my portrait put on a gold snuff-
box . . . the gold may cost you twenty louis." [15]

The contributions of another collaborator, a very major one,
the Englishman John Turberville Needham, will be discussed in
detail in the course of this study.

IV   *A Constricted Personal Life*

Hérault de Séchelles observed, after his visit with Buffon, "His
example and his own statements have convinced me that he who
desires glory passionately will, in the end, obtain it . . . but one
must desire it strongly, and that for no short time; one must desire it strongly every day of one's life." [16] Buffon's career was a
monument to this creed. As we have seen, he forced his life into

a rigid mold, determined that no possibility of productivity should be lost. Nevertheless, though a man may impose extreme limitations on his private life, he cannot eliminate it entirely, and Buffon did not escape the experiences that are common to almost all men. He was not only an author and an administrator, but also a friend, a husband, a father, and a lover, however much he may have begrudged the time these functions demanded.

Buffon's marriage is strangely reminiscent of his father's that he had so bitterly denounced in 1732, when his father at the age of fifty had married an almost penniless girl of twenty-two. In 1752, when all his many affairs were at last going smoothly, Buffon at the age of forty-five married an almost penniless girl of twenty, Marie-Françoise de Saint-Belin-Malain. He had fallen in love with her two years earlier, when she had been a student at the Ursuline convent in Montbard directed by Buffon's sister Jeanne, and he had conducted a successful courtship despite the interference and disapproval of Jeanne. "You shall see, my dear sir," he wrote to Gueneau de Montbeillard, "that the criticisms of my marriage disturb me even less than those of my books." The marriage was a happy one, for the humble young woman demanded little of her very famous and exceedingly busy husband. "Content with the single pleasures of loving and of admiring the man she loved," slyly noted Buffon's old enemy Condorcet in the eulogy he delivered in the Académie des Sciences after Buffon's death, "her heart was closed to all personal vanity." [17]

Their first child, a daughter, died in infancy, at seventeen months in October, 1759. "I have lost a child," Buffon wrote to Ruffey, "who was just beginning to make herself understood, which is to say, to make herself loved." The birth of their second, and last, child, the son affectionately called "Buffonet," on May 22, 1764, marked for Mme de Buffon the beginning of a long illness that terminated only with her death in 1769. Humbert-Bazile of Montbard, one of the last of Buffon's secretaries, was only a boy at the time of the death of Mme de Buffon, but he vividly recalled Buffon's tenderness to the dying woman: "M. de Buffon displayed toward her a kindness that touched all who witnessed it. He tried not to let his face reveal any signs of anguish that devoured his soul, and he dropped by every moment he had free from his work, and he would send a servant . . . to see how she was when he was prevented from doing so himself." [18] To the cynic, Humbert's encomium might suggest a few doubts, particularly the reference to the servants used as messengers. "I fear," Buffon had written to the Abbé Le Blanc in March 1738, "everything that can cause me to lose time."

Buffon's only son was a source of continual disappointment, for he lacked not only the great intellectual gifts Buffon had hoped for but even the common sense that the average father is led to expect. He was scatterbrained, wildly affectionate, an alarming spendthrift, an extravagantly reckless horseman and hunter for whom no fence was ever too high and no horse ever fast enough, apparently destined for an early death impaled on a hedgerow or drowned in a ditch, with barely the intellectual faculties needed for a modest career in the army of the *ancien régime*. But Buffon never lost hope that this crackbrained child of his old age would become one of the great scientists of France, perhaps by a miraculous metamorphosis similar to that which had transformed his own youth. He engaged for "Buffonet" the finest tutors he could find, including the brilliant young botanist Lamarck, the future evolutionist, who quickly proved unequal to the strain. Buffon also sent his son on a whole series of Grand Tours, confident that travel would have a broadening, or at least a sobering, effect. The boy was Buffon's emissary to Voltaire at Ferney, to the court of Prussia, and to the court of Catherine the Great of Russia, who had requested a bust of Buffon for her collection, which Buffonet delivered. Catherine found the youth a startling phenomenon; in a letter to Baron Grimm, she remarked upon the strange irony by which men of genius seem fated always to father sons who are virtual imbeciles.

In no way daunted, happily expectant, Buffon had very early taken steps to secure for his son the eventual succession to his post of superintendent of the Jardin du Roi. In February, 1771, when a violent attack of dysentery placed Buffon at what seemed to be death's door, the government voided the promises made and appointed Charles-Claude de Flahaut, Comte de la Billarderie d'Angeviller, the special favorite of the Dauphin, to the succession in the event of Buffon's death. Buffon would never reconcile himself completely to this *fait accompli*, which he regarded as the result of machinations steeped in infamy. Upon his unexpected recovery, the government, anxious to pacify the indignant superintendent, seeing in him a writer potentially as dangerous as Diderot or Voltaire, elevated his Burgundian estates, in July 1772, into a county, conferring the title of *count* upon both Buffon and his son,[19] and, as a further sop to the famed Buffonian vanity, a commission for a statue of Buffon to be erected at the Jardin du Roi was given at this time to the sculptor Pajou. The statue was completed and in place by 1777. It is still a conspicuous ornament of the institution.

When Buffonet neared twenty, still a hopeless wastrel, Buffon purchased a commission for him in the Gardes Françaises. Some years earlier he had begun genealogical inquiries into the background of the Leclerc family to find the *preuves de noblesse* so necessary at that time to a successful military career, to all appearances, the only career possible for Buffonet, but he had abandoned the effort when the early results proved decidedly unpromising." [20]

His son's first marriage, in 1784, was the occasion for a second clash with the centers of power, which Buffon had spent a lifetime conciliating. Buffonet's teen-aged wife, the daughter of the Marquis de Cepoy, soon made no secret of the fact that she was the mistress of the Duke of Orléans, later famous as Philippe Egalité, and Buffonet was not able to carry off the role of cuckold to royalty with any dignity. Positive action was unavoidable. Buffon ordered his son, in a letter of June 22, 1787, to resign his commission and travel somewhere, anywhere, until the scandal had died down. A new military commission was later purchased for him in a regiment less directly dependent upon the royal family. It is possible that even Buffon had at this juncture, a year before his death, ceased to believe that a brilliant future awaited his son. After the French Revolution had begun, Buffonet obtained a divorce and married Betzy Daubenton, a grandniece of Louis Daubenton, his father's first collaborator. In 1794, a victim of the Jacobin Terror and the malice of his dead father's old enemies, Buffonet died on the guillotine. He had been able to do little in his lifetime that had pleased his father, but even that most exigent of fathers could not have faulted his death. A true aristocrat, he walked to his death with calm resolution, and, on the scaffold itself, he had turned to shout with fierce pride to the spectators, "Citizens, my name is Buffon."

Buffon had apparently long foreseen the revolution that was to destroy the remnants of his own family. According to the Abbé

Soulavie, "Buffon . . . said to me in December, 1778, that this [coming] revolution would direct its first efforts against the French clergy, and advised me to take care of myself." [21] He foresaw the industrial revolution as well, even to the extent of investing, and losing, a large sum of money in a coal-mining venture that proved to be too far ahead of its time. But his interests bound him inextricably to the established *régime,* to the old ways and the old manners.

An aspect of the social life of the old order with which Buffon's name has always been prominently associated is the fashionable Parisian salon. This is not as paradoxical as it might seem. A writer so much in vogue, Buffon could not afford to lose touch with his public, and the bulk of his readers were members of the privileged classes; many were habitués of the great salons. Then too, Buffon's thirst for glory did not exclude a taste for the flattery of his contemporaries. The theatrical flair of this indefatigable toiler compelled him to seek out responsive audiences, even at the cost of a substantial waste of valuable working time.

In the period of his early successes Buffon was a familiar figure in the salons of Mme Geoffrin, Mme d'Epinay, and Baron d'Holbach, all as notable for wit and elegance as for advanced ideas. Toward the end of his career he favored the somewhat heavier atmosphere of the salon of Mme Necker. William Beckford, author of the exotic and sophisticated *Vathek,* penned a rather depressing portrait of this salon:

. . . the great doors of the grand saloon flying open discovered a synod of sallow literati in full court dress, and a row of long waisted pink and yellow dowagers, all seated on fauteuils composed of the stiffest tapestry, all taking deliberate pinches of snuff at frequent intervals, and all determined to cross examine poor unfortunate me as if I had been actually expected to take degrees in their supremely dull coterie. In this exemplary task they were aided and abetted by Buffon, de Lalande, and a host of savants their literary confessors. Zoology, Geology, and Meteorology formed the chief topics discussed, but tautology prevailed over all, for the same statements were repeated over and over and over again, every time, it appeared to me, with additional driness. [22]

For Buffon any hint of stodginess in the salon was more than amply compensated for by the presence of Mme Necker herself.

From the early 1770's until his death Buffon cherished an ardent affection, lavishly expressed in his letters, for this charming, pious, and opinionated woman, some thirty years younger than himself and the wife of a close friend, the Swiss banker upon whose financial genius the last hopes of the *ancien régime* were founded. This supreme romantic attachment in the life of Buffon was unquestionably platonic in nature, for the character of Mme Necker, unlike that of her remarkable daughter, the future Mme de Staël, was beyond reproach. Yet Mme Necker enjoyed the game of platonic love no less than Buffon. Her admiration for her elderly admirer knew no bounds. "M. de Buffon," she noted in her journal, "has never spoken to me of the marvels of the earth without inspiring in me the thought that he himself was one of them." [23] The fires of his virtuous passion (the French would call it *"une amitié amoureuse"*) rekindled in Buffon a taste for composing Latin verse, learned more than sixty years before at the *collège* in Dijon (*"Angelica facies et formoso corpore Necker. . . ."*).

During his last illness, through the periods of extreme pain caused by the kidney stones that at length killed him, Buffon found in the constant presence of Mme Necker his one solace. Each morning she came to his apartments at the Jardin du Roi to sit at his bedside. "What kindness!" he would say, "You come to watch me die. What a spectacle for a sensitive soul!" In effect, she not only watched but recorded the spectacle, even to the most gruesome details of Buffon's tormented last moments, as he made his final confession and, almost hysterical with pain and despair, received the last rites from the Capuchin Ignace. She seems to have found this extraordinary mixture of delirium and religiosity an edifying spectacle, as Buffon had hoped, and her admiration for him was strengthened. "Sometimes still," she later wrote to Lord Stormont, a mutual friend, "his great soul rises from the midst of his ashes to commune with me." [24]

CHAPTER 5

Genesis Revised—From Seven Days to Seven Epochs

I *Pliable Data from "Physical Romances"*

BUFFON'S longest and most ambitious project within his central work, the *Histoire Naturelle,* was his attempt to extract a simple and straightforward account of the origin and development of the "terraqueous globe" from data drawn from the almost brand-new earth sciences of his time. The first essay to be completed, *La Théorie de la Terre* (H.N. I), was dated 1744, and the definitive essay, the most famous of all his essays, the *Epoques de la Nature* (H.N.S. V), was published in 1778, a third of a century later.[1]

These essays represented Buffon's one departure from a lifelong policy of avoiding trouble in any form whatsoever. They involved him in difficulties, dangerous difficulties, with the ecclesiastical authorities and made him a favorite target for a host of polemicists, both religious and scientific.

But the field of cosmogony, the elaboration of a general theory explaining both the origin and "mechanism" of the solar system and the earth itself, the whence and the how, seemed to offer an opportunity to "complete" the work of Sir Isaac Newton, to add something new, something distinctly Buffonian, to the fundamental principles of the "New Physics" created by Newton, and thus to assume, in the eyes of future generations, a stature equal to that of Newton himself. The engraved portrait of Newton that hung over Buffon's writing desk in the ancient tower at Montbard was, quite simply, a practical reminder of a heroic aspiration.

Unlike Newton, however, Buffon was concerned in this field almost entirely with the interpretation of detailed data furnished by others. And what was probably his greatest imaginative effort was given a somewhat speciously inductive cast, doubly suspect since the works he drew the data from were themselves highly imaginative and "literary." The data sources came at first largely from England and northern Europe, predominantly Protestant states in which the New Science was long regarded chiefly as a useful adjunct to the old theology. The few systematic observations involved had been gathered in great part by men whose primary concern was in "documenting" certain biblical accounts, like Noah's Flood. During Buffon's lifetime, though, owing in some degree to his own efforts, cosmogony and earth science became extremely popular subjects in France, and French sources took on new importance. In the first volume of the *Histoire Naturelle* (1749), the distribution of source works was approximately as follows: English, 34 percent; French, 30 percent; Ancients, 14 percent; others, 22 percent. In the fifth volume of *Suppléments* (1778), the distribution had become: English, 15 percent; French, 46 percent; Ancients, 9 percent; others, 30 percent. The number of references to English authors in particular decreases rapidly as one proceeds through the *Histoire Naturelle*. References to ancient authors also decrease, but much more slowly. Throughout his career, Buffon held to the theory that an immense corpus of science had existed in the ancient world, of which only a few remnants, essentially compendia, had survived, and he habitually cited ancient Greek and Roman authors with the same respect he accorded to his most distinguished contemporaries.

In a preliminary discussion of the sources, Buffon singled out the Englishman Thomas Burnet, author of the *Telluris Theoria Sacra* (1681), translated into English by its author as *The Sacred Theory of the Earth* in 1684, as "the first to have treated this matter in a general and systematic manner," choosing to ignore the widely known fact that Burnet's work was little more than a theologian's reworking of earlier writings by René Descartes. Burnet's work had been the object of an extremely savage controversy among British theologians and scientists, and Buffon seems to have relied heavily on "refutations" of Burnet, particularly those of the mathematician John Keill, for much of his own information. Like Keill, who labeled Burnet's work "a philosophical romance," Buffon praised Burnet's style, "But to return to Burnet, his book is elegantly written; he knows how to paint, how to present great images forcefully and bring magnificent scenes before our eyes," and condemned the substance, "a well written romance, a book which may be read for pleasure, but which ought not to be consulted with a view to instructing oneself" (H.N. I, p. 181).

Another Englishman, John Woodward, a hardheaded medical man and rather reluctant opponent of Burnet, had produced a wildly improbable theory that dominated British cosmogony for almost a century. Woodward was perhaps Buffon's single most important source. His observations on fossils and rock formations are cited seventeen times in the first volume of the *Histoire Naturelle* alone, though Buffon occasionally indulged in scathing sarcasm in his rapid review of Woodward's *An Essay towards a Natural History of the Earth* of 1693 (H.N. I, pp. 183–87). Woodward was one of the many early English cosmogonists who attempted to relate every topographic feature of the present earth to the biblical Flood, but Woodward's Flood was more than equal to the demands he made upon it: "The whole Terrestrial Globe was taken all to Pieces and dissolved at the Deluge, the Particles of Stone, Marble, and all other solid Fossils being dissevered, taken up into the Water, and there sustained together with Sea-Shells and other Animal and Vegetable Bodyes." [2] The direct cause of this remarkable event, insisted Woodward, could only have been the Divine Will, effecting a temporary abrogation of Newton's law of attraction, which, once re-established, brought all this suspended matter down again, this time arranged in strata according to specific gravity. The one real point of difficulty in the theory was the evident failure of the sea shells and other animal remains to dissolve during the time Nature's laws were suspended, and this was resolved by Woodward through his insistence upon an essential (and mysterious) difference between inorganic and organic materials, a distinction that brought him close to Buffon's own later theory of organic molecules.

Buffon also quickly reviewed, generally hostilely, William Whiston's *New Theory of the Earth* (1696), a particularly imaginative work which explained the Flood itself as the result of a collision of the earth with a water-laden comet, but Buffon's stern strictures on Whiston's "charlatanism" were not unmixed with notes of admiration: "One shall always be astonished that, from a *mélange* of ideas so bizarre and so little fashioned to consort together, it was possible to extract a truly dazzling system" (H.N. I, p. 170).

Buffon did not discuss at any length the *Three Physico-Theological Discourses* 1692, 1693) of the great John Ray, but he did cite the work repeatedly in the *Théorie de la Terre*. The crux of Ray's system was the ancient theory, variously assignable to Aristotle or Anaximenes, of endless mutual encroachments of land upon sea and of sea upon land, by which an eventual change of positions is effected: "Equality is still constantly maintained, notwithstanding all Inundations of Land, and Alterations of Sea; because one of these doth always nearly ballance the other, according to the vulgar Proverb we have before mention'd, *What the Sea loses in one place, it gains in another.*" [3] Ray's theory, or "vulgar proverb," with its vision of a world ceaselessly shaped and reshaped by restless waters, was in essence the first position taken by Buffon himself in the slow evolution of his thought toward the definitive *Epoques de la Nature*.

II   *The Launching of the Epochs—The Universal Sea*

In 1778, in the *Epoques de la Nature*, Buffon defined seven stages or *époques* in earth history, that is, a molten stage, a too-hot-to-touch stage, a universal-sea stage, a volcanic upheaval stage, a stage characterized by the emergence of land animals, a stage of widespread subsidence, or sinking, of landmasses, during which the present continents were defined, and, finally, the age of man. The completed theory had itself emerged by stages, one by one, in a confused, haphazard way, each *époque* taking its development from some particular facet of the author's varied activities.

The first of the seven *époques* of the theory to emerge was the third, the universal-sea stage, for this was the main subject of the original essay, the *Théorie de la Terre*. In Buffon's usage in the 1740's the word *théorie* was not a synonym for *hypothesis* or *system*, both anathema to him at that time; it quite specifically designated "a close induction from established facts." He clearly felt himself to be on distinctly different ground from Whiston, Woodward *et al.*, felt indeed that he had succeeded in extracting, and properly ordering, the few kernels of truth embedded in their wild lucubrations.

The two keystone "facts" of this theoretical structure which he considered so solid were Woodward's detailed observations of the "horizontal" strata of the earth's crust and the Frenchman Louis Bourguet's discovery that the angles described by the slopes of neighboring hills often display some degree of correspondence. Woodward's orderly strata, studded "everywhere" with fossil shells, and Bourguet's neatly corresponding angles seemed to Buffon to prove, beyond question, first that the topography of all the exposed land areas of the earth had been determined at a time when they lay at the bottom of the sea, and, second, that almost all of the features of the land were due to slow, progressive sedimentation and the molding effect of powerful ocean currents, currents whose shaping pressures would always be distributed equally to the right and to the left as they carved valleys in the ocean floor.

Completely satisfied with the validity of this central position, Buffon attempted few theoretical embellishments. The early *Théorie de la Terre* was rigorously conservative: "We can thus judge only the outermost, almost superficial layer; the interior of the earth is entirely unknown to us" (H.N. I, p. 70). There was involved in Buffon's early "Neptunism," the belief that water alone, unaided by fire, had sculpted the earth's surface, a strong emotional predisposition, an inland man's awe of the sea's enormous power. Buffon's experience of the sea had been quite limited, but immensely affecting. In his tour through Italy in 1731–32 in company with the young Duke of Kingston and Dr. Hickman he had witnessed a great storm in the port of Leghorn:

I have seen, I say, the waters of the sea lift themselves above ramparts which had appeared to me to be at a very considerable elevation above the waters, and, as I was on those which are the most advanced, I was not able to regain the city without being drenched with sea water far more thoroughly than one could ever be by the most abundant rain. (H.N. I, p. 437)

In the course of this storm, Buffon saw several large ships stripped of their rigging and masts and torn from their moorings within the protected harbor itself, all of this in an area "where the sea is more tranquil and where there is no tide."

Furthermore, Woodward was Buffon's most important source,

and Woodward's writings radiated confidence: "The next Cole-
pit, or Mine, the next Quarry, or Chalk-pit, will give abundant
Attestations to what I write." [4] Had Buffon lived some few miles
farther to the east, in the high mountains, his faith in Woodward's
observations might have been less absolute, but the rare, casual,
and rather picnicky field trips and "digs" that Buffon made in the
hills and valleys of his native Burgundy offered full confirmation
of everything the Englishman had found in his own island. Only
many years later, in 1778 in the *Additions et Corrections aux
Preuves de la Théorie de la Terre,* did Buffon formally free himself from Woodward's influence:

I am able to say that, in general, there is no change to be made in my
entire Theory of the Earth beyond that which regards the composition
of the first mountains, which owe their origin to the primitive fire, and
not to the action of water as I had conjectured, for I was then persuaded by the authority of Woodward and of several other naturalists
that sea shells were to be found on every mountain top. (H.N.S. V,
p. 320)

It was, however, too late.

By 1778 Buffon's hypothetical primitive ocean, quite small in
1744, had become "that universal sea": "The waters covered the
entire surface of the globe to a height of two thousand fathoms
above the level of our present seas; the earth was then under the
empire of the sea" (H.N.S. V, 132). Why precisely two thousand
fathoms? Buffon had set the depth of his primitive universal sea
at exactly the maximum altitude at which fossil shells had been
found. Never did he appear less "modern," less the true scientist.
He had simply assumed that all the sedimentary rocks of the
globe had remained in essentially the same position since the
time of their deposition, totally discounting the possibility of
major upheavals of the earth's surface. And this crucial error
seems to have stemmed directly from his reading of Woodward,
to judge from the manner of some of Buffon's citations: "He
[Woodward] saw that these strata were horizontal and rested
one on top of the other, as material would be that had been
transported by water and deposited in the form of sediments"
(H.N. I, p. 184). In point of fact, however, Woodward himself,
despite the requirements of his own theory, had often drastically
qualified such statements, though he did habitually use the term

horizontal in a very careless fashion, as a convenient synonym
for *parallel:* "I call those *Fissures* . . . *Horizontal* . . . not so
much with respect to the *present* Site of the *Strata,* which is
alter'd, in many Places, and now much different from their original Situation."[5] Perhaps appropriately, the major error in Buffon's cosmogony, this cosmogony drawn from his readings, is
traceable to a simple misreading, or misinterpretation, of a source
work. Even more fundamentally, though, the error may be attributed to Buffon's tendency to assume a degree of order and simplicity in geological processes that only books could have suggested, and that more extensive and serious field trips would have
corrected. His errors in theoretical geology are bookish errors.

III   *Planets and Comets*

Article I of the *"Preuves de la Théorie de la Terre,"* published
in the first volume of the *Histoire Naturelle* in 1749, opens with
a proposition, which, even assuming that it was intended primarily for the eyes of ecclesiastical censors, seems far removed from
the spirit of Baconian induction, or from any other narrowly
empirical approach:

One will find in this volume extracts from so many systems and from
so many hypotheses . . . that one cannot find it objectionable if we
here join our conjectures to those of the philosophers who have written
on this matter, above all when it is understood that we in effect present
them as simple conjectures, to which we pretend to attach no more
than a greater degree of probability than is to be found in all those
that have previously been proposed on the same subject.

The subject in question was the origin of the planets, a matter
admittedly more suited to speculation than experimentation,
though Buffon would actually employ both approaches. His first
step was, characteristically, an assembling and ordering of the
"givens" in the manner of a mathematician. The essential "given"
appeared to be that, so far as eighteenth-century astronomers
knew, the planets all move around the sun in the same direction
and in roughly the same plane: "This conformity of position and
direction in the movement of the planets suggests necessarily
something in common in their movement of impulsion, and should
make one suspect that it was communicated to them all by a
single and same cause" (H.N. I, p. 133). The cause itself seemed

equally evident: a comet, colliding with the sun and hurling a number of fragments from the sun's surface out into space where, once their initial momentum had slackened, the sun's attraction tugged them to a halt and dragged them into orbital paths determined by equilibrium between the "movement of impulsion" and the gravitational pull. Buffon cited Newton himself as the source of the notion that "comets occasionally fall upon the sun" (H.N. I, p. 135).

Buffon's contemporary opponents, as unaware as he of the relative insubstantiality of comets, also turned to Newton's works, and found a major objection to Buffon's theory in Newton's pronouncement that any projectile fired from the surface of a heavenly body must necessarily return periodically to its point of origin. Buffon, ardent Newtonian that he was, had attempted to anticipate the objection: "To that I reply that the matter that composes the planets did not leave the sun as fully formed globes to which the comet communicated its movement of impulsion, but that the matter left in the form of a torrent, the movement of its anterior parts accelerated by that of the posterior sections" (H.N. I, p. 139). As might be expected, the explanation proved more acceptable to Cartesians, fully accustomed to "torrents of matter," than to Newtonians.

In many places, Buffon's speculations on the nature of matter bring him very close to Descartes' very imaginative original writings, if not to the exclusively mechanistic matter-in-motion views of eighteenth-century Cartesians. In 1774, for example, Buffon wrote:

One must conclude that all matter can become light, heat, fire. . . . Thus light, heat, and fire are not particular kinds of matter, different from all other matter; they are but matter, which is ever the same, that has undergone no alteration, no modification, beyond that of a great division into parts. . . . (H.N.S. I, p. 11)

Buffon's occasional recourse to "torrents" of matter, matter that is divisible but changeless, did not mean, however, that he had abandoned Newton for Descartes. A vast gap in his cosmogony remained to be filled, the one that separated the original fiery mass, which had been hurled free of the sun by his comet, from the alternately drowned and dank globe pictured in the *Théorie de la Terre*. And Newton, in a little-known passage of the *Principia*, had suggested the course to follow:

A globe of red-hot iron equal to our earth, that is, about 40000000 feet in diameter, would scarcely cool in an equal number of days, or in above 50000 years. But I suspect that the duration of heat may, on account of some latent causes, increase in a yet less ratio than that of the diameter; and I should be glad that the true ratio was investigated by experiments.[6]

The "globe" Sir Isaac had had in mind was a comet's nucleus, but the possible application of the experiments he had suggested to Buffon's own hypothetical sun fragments was inescapable. And Buffon, since 1767 the proud proprietor of one of the finest commercial foundries in France, executed the experiments with munificence and zeal. Several decades later, in a eulogy of Buffon delivered in the Académie Française, Vicq d'Azyr expatiated upon "that love of the great that distinguished him. To estimate the strength and endurance of wood he subjected entire forests to his experiments. To obtain new results on the progress of heat, he placed enormous metal globes upon torrents of flame and smoke." [7] In actual fact, the "enormous globes," some two dozen of them, each of a different substance, were "all of one inch in diameter" (H.N.S. I, p. 173).

The procedure followed in these heat calibration experiments, though, was sufficiently dramatic. The quantity to be measured was the time elapsed between the moment when the balls were removed, white hot, from the furnaces to "the moment in which one could touch them and hold them in one's hand," surely an experiment few would care to repeat. The Chevalier Aude, who spent a few weeks at Montbard late in Buffon's life in the ambiguous role of guest and secretary, gave a scandalous and "*sadique*" account of these experiments, performed a quarter of a century before his passage:

To determine the epoch of the formation of the planets and to calculate the cooling time of the terrestrial globe, he had resort to four or five pretty women, with very soft skin; he had several balls, of all sorts of matters and all sorts of densities, heated red rot, and they held these in turns in their delicate hands, while describing to him the degrees of heat and cooling.[8]

Whatever the details of methodology might have been, the experiments yielded results that were, in their exactitude, all that an experimenter with singed fingers could desire:

Instead of the 50,000 years which he [Newton] assigns for the time required to cool the earth to its present temperature, it would require 42,964 years and 221 days to cool it just to the point at which it ceased to burn. (H.N.S. I, 157)

These estimates of the time needed for the molten earth to cool and solidify, based on actual experiments, formed the nucleus of the time schedule Buffon laid down for his cosmogony, his famous "milestones on time's eternal highway" (H.N.S. V, p. 1).

This extremely precise time scheme, a product of thought often unduly and naïvely awed by "experiment," is responsible in large part for the air of quaint antiquity the *Epoques de la Nature* enjoys today. Buffon's final figure for the age of the earth, 74,832 years, can only seem preposterously inadequate to a modern reader. For every year of Buffon's published estimate more recent geologists would substitute at least twenty millennia. But, in an age that confidently placed the events of Genesis in the year 4004 B.C., Buffon's estimate was audacious—though not reckless. Curiously, for Buffon possessed to a supreme degree the arts of persuasion, the figures are never convincing. The attentive reader soon perceives that this is so because Buffon himself is constantly challenging them, suggesting nagging doubts at the very moment he advances his precise figures. Pierre Flourens, the most dedicated and influential of the nineteenth-century editors of the *Histoire Naturelle*, found, in studying the few surviving manuscripts of the *Epoques de la Nature*, that Buffon had actually contemplated using figures as much as three hundred times as great as those in the printed versions.[9] And these manuscripts, now in the library of the Muséum National d'Histoire Naturelle in Paris, offer evidence that even larger figures, up to infinity itself, were considered. Buffon drastically and prudently reduced the estimates, he himself noted in the manuscript, solely to avoid shocking his readers and giving his work an air of wild fantasy. The division of the time scheme into seven periods, a number inevitably reminiscent of the seven days of Genesis, was almost certainly dictated by similar esthetic, and politic, considerations,

and is not to be considered among the basic concepts advanced
in the work. Nor should it be forgotten that since the first volume
of the *Histoire Naturelle* theologians had been snapping at his
heels because of ideas that ran counter to the Book of Genesis.

IV *Out of Primal Heat, the Age of Life*

A secondary, though extremely important, result of Buffon's
Newton-inspired heat experiments was the final admission into his
cosmogony of the hypothesis of the internal heat of the earth.
Almost without exception, Buffon's predecessors in cosmogony,
the authors of his source books, had postulated molten central
cores for their terraqueous globes. In the beginning Buffon had
apparently been warned off this position by the doubts expressed
by Keill and Ray. Buffon's early geological essays set very rigid
limits on speculation, treating, as we have seen, only the "exterior, almost superficial layer" of the earth. A quarter of a century later, however, not only was the internal heat of the earth
accepted as fact by Buffon, but it was also credited with the key
role in the original formation of the "organic molecules," the
microscopic building blocks of life, through the transformation
of ordinary molecules. In addition, Buffon directly linked such
disparate earth phenomena as electricity, magnetism, and the
perpendicular growth of plants to the internal heat of the globe.

The most conspicuous reason for the change in Buffon's position on internal heat was the publication in 1765 of Dortous de
Mairan's final results, formidably documented, on climatic and
seasonal variations in temperature. Mairan had established, to the
full satisfaction of his scientific contemporaries, that there was a
regular discrepancy, a constant and easily measurable gap, between the differences in temperature in summer and winter in
any area and the differences in the amount of sunlight received.
These discrepancies formed the basis for his exact calibration of
the "emanations" of the earth's central fire. Mairan's prestige as
a physicist was immense, and his endless batteries of meteoro-
logical tables are still overwhelmingly impressive; at one stroke,
he had rendered the internal heat hypothesis completely respectable. Yet, his colleagues had been familiar with his earlier results
for many years; Mairan's much publicized 1765 *mémoire*, published by the Académie Royale des Sciences, was ostensibly a
supplement to a *mémoire* published in 1719 and a *dissertation*

published in 1749. What Mairan provided was probably more the occasion than the major reasons for Buffon's reappraisal. In Buffon's mind, through the years, his comet theory had evidently come to seem less and less a theory and more and more a fact. This is, of course, the process by which novels and dramas are born, and here again Buffon seems closer to the *littérateur* than to the scientist. By the 1760's he was prepared to accept, as facts, the ultimate implications of his conviction that the earth had been formed from a fragment of the sun, and these implications clearly included the persistence of some remnants of original heat, lodged deep within the globe. The heat experiments Buffon performed in the late 1760's also reflect this renewed commitment to his early "theories." Had astral collision remained a simple hypothesis in his thought, it could hardly have supported the elaborate machinery he was shortly to erect upon it.

These changes in viewpoint were also manifested in changes in Buffon's explanations of volcanoes. In the first volume of the *Histoire Naturelle* he had attributed all volcanic activity to the chemical action of ground water on deposits of combustible material. He had even suggested an amusing experiment, in which a small amount of sulphur, covered with dirt, could be induced to form a miniature volcano by lightly sprinkling it with water (H.N. I, pp. 113, 502–35). Few phenomena could be more simple: "A volcano is an immense cannon." In the *Epoques,* however, our newly experienced foundry proprietor and thermal experimenter is prepared to encounter a much higher level of complexity. Happily, he finds volcanoes can still be explained by analogies, though slightly more sophisticated analogies, drawn from wider experience: "A volcano is only a vast furnace, whose bellows, or rather ventilators, are placed in caverns far below . . . these same caverns, when they extend to the sea, serve as exhaust pipes" (H.N.S. V, p. 137). The newly acknowledged central heat of the globe enters this picture in the form of terrestrial electricity, basically a finer or subtler form of heat, which ignites the pockets of combustible matter that still serve as the essential fuel for the volcano's fires. An explosion, the eruption itself, occurs only when large volumes of water find their way into the heart of the mechanism by way of the subterranean passages connecting with the sea. So confident was Buffon of the accuracy of this "reconstruction" that he ventured to suggest that the governments of Europe undertake to construct barriers across the water-filled underground passageways of all dangerous volcanoes, a project that struck him as not substantially more difficult than the building of the pyramids (H.N.S. V, p. 140).

In constructing his general theory, into which he hoped to fit all the data of all the sciences, Buffon returned again and again to a few basic concepts, in the most widely diverse contexts, weaving, as it were, into the matrix of his ideas, in which all is interconnected, a few brightly colored fibers that are seemingly without end. The idea of the progressive cooling of our globe, itself a derivative of the comet hypothesis, is one of these master strands. He extrapolated from it, once he had fully accepted its reality, not only explanations of volcanoes and climatic anomalies, but also, ranging far afield, a plausible explanation of the fossilized remains of huge land animals, a phenomenon he had largely ignored in the *Théorie de la Terre*.

If one assumes that the polar extremities of the earth once enjoyed tropic heat, it becomes possible to identify the strange and gigantic bones found in northern snows with species today found only in equatorial regions. And, if these ancient animals were obviously much larger than any animal presently living, this can only be because the productive capacities of Nature are proportionate to the earth's temperature, warmer periods producing larger animals. Since Buffon had assumed that heat alone was sufficient to transform ordinary molecules into "organic" molecules, molecules endowed with the capacity to assemble themselves spontaneously into living creatures, it did not seem at all unreasonable to assume that higher degrees of heat must needs produce larger animals and plants.

Buffon then proceeded to use the geographical distribution of all the prehistoric "elephant" remains known to eighteenth-century paleontologists to pinpoint, on the timetable he had already established for the progressive cooling of the globe, the "epoch" of the formation of the present continental masses. He judged, from what he had deduced concerning the rate of cooling of the distant northern regions in which elephants or—a matter of little real importance—creatures essentially like elephants, must have first appeared (for the equatorial regions would still have been too hot to support any life at the time), that the great beasts must have been obliged, by the increasing severity of northern winters, to start their southward trek approximately ten thousand years ago. The Eurasian, American, and African landmasses must, therefore, have been joined together at that time, in one great continent, and the interposition of the waters of the Atlantic and the Mediterranean must have occurred shortly after the animal migrations (H.N.S. V, p. 206).

The abrupt disappearance of the enormous land bridges that once linked all the major continents is the spectacular central event of the sixth "epoch." Like all the pivotal concepts of the *Epoques de la Nature*, it was an old idea slowly matured. The question of the subsidence beneath the sea of extensive land masses is briefly treated in the first volume of the *Histoire Naturelle* in connection with the hypothesis of an ancient marsh connecting France and England. British scientists of the seventeenth century had collected so much data supporting the Channel marsh hypothesis that by Buffon's day it was generally regarded as a fully established fact. Plato's legend of Atlantis was also briefly discussed by Buffon in the first volume, with fossil evidence cited in support of it (H.N. I, p. 606). But, in the early stages of his theory, Buffon, then a doctrinaire "Neptunist," totally committed to water as the unique molding agent of all topographical features, preferred to explain subsidence solely in terms of the inexorable shifting of the boundaries of the seas, discounting almost entirely the role played by earthquakes, or diastrophism in general, the raising or lowering of the surface of the earth itself, since water alone, however agitated, could not conceivably effect such changes. In the absence of what to him seemed plausible and possible mechanisms, Buffon did not at first hesitate to leave gaps in his theory. Full acceptance of the concept of a world formed by the solidification of molten matter, however, removed this difficulty: "In the first moments in which its surface began to take on some consistency, irregularities must have formed, such as one sees on the surface of substances that have been melted and recooled" (H.N.S. I, p. 122). These "irregularities," or giant earth blisters, could account not only for certain mountains and plateaus, but for vast subterranean caverns as well, caverns whose subsequent collapse provides a completely satisfactory mechanism for sudden and violent subsidence.

But Buffon's cooling, "vitreous" globe, vilified as "the glass world" by contemporary critics, in addition to resolving some standing difficulties, also posed a few new problems. How was one to deal, for example, with unchallengeable historical evidence that suggested that the Gaul of Vercingetorix and Caesar, who had fought their last great battle only a few miles from the future site of the Count de Buffon's château eighteen centuries before, was far colder in all seasons than modern France, instead of being much hotter, as Buffon's theory seemingly demanded? Not unexpectedly, Buffon quickly found an answer, a quintessentially Buffonian answer: climatic changes can be brought about by man's own activities, such as the clearing of forests, the damming of rivers, and the erecting of cities. He believed that similar changes were already occurring in Canada, as more and more settlements were established there.

From the very beginning Buffon's thought had been primarily subjective, basically man centered. An intense awareness that "Nature" is essentially human experience led him to place man at the focal point of all his investigations. His major contribution as a mathematician was to introduce into probability calculations the factor of the relative importance of the events to the people involved; he added the study of aberrations in the functioning of the human eye to the study of colors, conducting experiments that damaged his own eyesight; in his first attempt at classifying animals he assumed that the only "rational" classification would be by order of the importance of the animals to man; as a theoretical physicist, he suggested that all the forces of nature were in fact one force, attributing all apparent diversity to man's imperfect perception. As the direct and inevitable result of this preoccupation with man as the focal point of all phenomena, Buffon arrived at a truly remarkable realization of the extent of man's power over his environment. Duly impressed by modifications man had produced in domesticated species of plants and animals, modifications thrown into high relief by his "rational" system of classification, he went on, not unnaturally, to hypothesize similar modifications in the land itself.

Buffon's seventh and last epoch, "when the power of man has seconded that of Nature," is thus the *terminus ad quem* both for the cosmogony and for the totality of Buffon's thought as well. His final vision, shared by such contemporaries as Thomas Jefferson, of a totally malleable Nature completely subjugated to the will of man, is at a far remove from the fashionable teleology of

the earlier cosmogonists from whom Buffon had taken most of his
data, however close to them Buffon may at times seem in specific
statements. The implications of his completed theory led Buffon,
in a rare prophetic vein, to foresee a glorious future, as heavily
populated nations with economies founded on the mining of coal,
for the frozen wastelands of North America and Siberia, lands
Voltaire had contemptuously dismissed as *"quelques arpents de
neige."* The enthusiasm with which Buffon looked forward to ever
greater triumphs of the human spirit in the centuries ahead
sprang from a fundamental optimism, the same optimism that
later led him to attribute the origin of society to nothing more sinister than mutual needs rationally perceived, the optimism that is
inseparable from the spirit of scientific inquiry.

V *A Defender of the Faith?*

"Our authors [Whiston, Woodward, Burnet] have made vain
efforts to account for the Deluge; their errors in physics with
regard to the secondary causes which they employ prove the
truth of the fact exactly as it is related in the Holy Scriptures, and
demonstrate that it could have been effected only by the primary
cause, by the Will of God." "The exposition which we have just
made suffices to demonstrate the contrariety which exists between
his [Whiston's] opinions and the Faith, and, consequently, the
insufficiency of his proofs." "To say that the sea formerly covered
all of the land, indeed that it covered the globe itself quite entirely, and that it is for this reason that one finds the shells of the
sea everywhere, this is to fail to take note of a very essential
point, which is the unity in point of time of the Creation." "All
truth coming equally from God, there is no difference between the
truths which He has revealed to us and those which He has permitted us to discover by our observations and our researches."

The author of these resoundingly pious pronouncements, this
"Defender of the Faith," is none other than the Count de Buffon,
exercising his outraged orthodoxy upon his British predecessors
in cosmogony (H.N. I, pp. 169, 196, 199; H.N.S. V, p. 35). They
represent only a very modest sampling; one could cull from the
Histoire Naturelle an entire breviary of ecclesiastical obscurant-
ism. Nearly a dozen pages of the *Epoques,* for example, are devoted to an attempt to "reconcile" Buffon's theory with Genesis,
an effort which, by an improbable complication of moral turpi-

tude, had been "borrowed," most indiscreetly, from an unpublished work of the dead encyclopedist Nicolas Boulanger.

What are we to think when confronted with Buffon in the role of a defender of the faith? Can we believe that he did in fact view the English cosmogonists with the horror of a Christian justly outraged at impious tampering with the revealed Word? Or can we regard Buffon's egregious, and often irrelevant, professions of faith as no more than justifiable subterfuges imposed by tyrannic censorship? This latter view has much to recommend it. There can be no doubt as to the reality or the seriousness of the danger Buffon faced from the moment his earliest efforts at cosmogony appeared.

As we have seen, the first volume of the *Histoire Naturelle* was the subject of an official inquiry by a committee of the Faculty of Theology of the University of Paris, popularly known as the Sorbonne. Buffon received a letter from this committee requesting clarification of certain "propositions" contained in his work. His reply to the Sorbonne, dated March 12, 1751, the Sorbonne's reply to his reply, the original letter, all appeared in Volume IV of the *Histoire Naturelle*. Buffon's success was total. He wrote Abbé Le Blanc, on April 24, 1751, in jubilant terms: "I have extricated myself to my very great satisfaction. Of one hundred and twenty assembled doctors, I had one hundred and fifteen, and their decision even contains words of praise for me, which I didn't expect." [10] Montesquieu, whose *Esprit des Lois* was the subject of a similar inquiry at the very same time, chose not to stoop, and saw his work officially condemned, placed on the Index of Prohibited Books.

The essential statement of Buffon's letter of conciliation to the Sorbonne conformed to a formula that had been "standard" for more than a century: "I abandon whatever in my book concerns the formation of the earth, and in general all that might be contrary to the narration of Moses, having presented my hypothesis on the formation of the planets only as a pure philosophical speculation." He was careful to insert the same statement into the introductory section of the *Epoques de la Nature,* but the temper of the times had changed. In November 1779, the *Epoques* was formally denounced before the faculty of theology, and a committee was appointed to consider the question of an official censure. Here, however, the matter rested. The king himself urged the committee to proceed with circumspection, an admonition that so impressed the assembled doctors that their committee never reported, some few taking covert revenge in dropping hints that the work had been judged the harmless product of senility.

Thus, Buffon successfully evaded the mailed fist of ecclesiastical authority with humble remonstrances, but his only weapon against the tonsured pamphleteers who repeatedly and zealously attacked the *Histoire Naturelle* was silence. Works such as Abbé Royou's *Le Monde de Verre de M. le comte de Buffon réduit en poudre* of 1780 or Abbé Feller's *Lettre critique sur l'Histoire Naturelle de Buffon* of 1773 made a bitter impression on the susceptible Buffon, but he judged, rightly as it proved, that they would not long waste their barbs on a victim who gave no sign of discomfiture. Buffon's tactics in these matters have struck certain of his critics as ignoble, but, in the century of the Chevalier de la Barre, Buffon published, in France and at the Imprimerie Royale, a pioneering work whose every conclusion, despite a plethora of disclaimers to the contrary, had been drawn uniquely from the laws that govern scientific inquiry.

A small number of Buffon's critics, however, have taken a radically different position. They have argued that he was truly a devout Catholic, and never a nimble politician in the realms of faith. In 1881, in a definitive article, *"La Religion de Buffon,"* Charles Barthélemy added his name to those of Humbert-Bazile, Chateaubriand, and Henri Nadault de Buffon, in the long list of those who had sought to establish the authenticity of Buffon's orthodoxy.[11] He cited the chapel established by Buffon at his foundry, the punctiliousness of his religious observances, his assiduity at the confessional, his death in odor of sanctity, and then triumphantly noted that the one substantial piece of evidence advanced by those who accused the great naturalist of the most infamous hypocrisy was a remark attested to only by Hérault de Séchelles. Hérault had quoted the elderly gentleman he visited at Montbard as remarking, doubtless in a highly confidential tone, that he regarded his declaration of faith to the Sorbonne in 1751 as only a *"persiflage."* In 1952, Jean Piveteau, in an article entitled *"La Pensée religieuse de Buffon"* included in the volume devoted to Buffon in the series *Les Grands Naturalistes Français* published

by the Muséum National d'Histoire Naturelle, took much the same
position as Barthélemy.[12]

Nevertheless, the vast mass of Buffon's own writing offers little
to support this view. The basic tenets that recur constantly
throughout the *Histoire Naturelle*, though not incompatible with
the faith of a Christian, do preclude naïvely literal scriptural
interpretations, and are at all times remote from the teachings of
the contemporary church. A belief in miracles could not, for instance, coexist with Buffon's confidence in the regularity and
orderliness of nature, his conviction that the study of the present
can completely elucidate both the past and the future: "Causes
whose effects are rare, violent and sudden need not concern us;
they are not found in Nature's regular progress" (H.N. I, p. 99).
He believed very firmly in the necessary autonomy of science,
finding abhorrent "the fault of wishing to mix physics with theology" (H.N. I, p. 197). In 1773, though fully convinced of his
personal competence in every area of natural science, he wrote to
the Abbé de Launay: "I do not understand theology, and I have
always abstained from discussing it." [13] In 1766, in a letter to
Charles de Brosses, he had singled out from the incomprehensible
corpus of abstract philosophy "the true metaphysics, and the only
one which is productive of light, which is to say, the metaphysics
drawn from nature." [14] There are, too, in Buffon's correspondence,
many denunciations of superstition and of rapacious priests.[15]

There is nothing in all of this, however, that suggests an aggressive atheism of the type professed by the Baron d'Holbach, that
"personal enemy" of God. There were clearly many components
of faith in Buffon's makeup. There was, above all, the awe before
the mystery and grandeur of the universe which he expressed with
sweeping poetic fervor in the great "Prayer" that closes the first
"Vue de la Nature," a reverent invocation to the "Great God,
whose sole *presence* [italics added] sustains nature and maintains
the harmony of the laws of the universe" (H.N. XII, p. xv). Perhaps, in the manner of the amateur of mathematical problems
he always remained, Buffon found the "givens" of the problems of
explicit religious affirmation somewhat insufficient and did not
care to attempt a solution.

In any event, Buffon definitely did not, in the fashion of Teilhard de Chardin in the twentieth century, attempt to find in his

meticulously ordered cosmogony the adumbration of a transcendental philosophy. In rewriting Genesis he ventured only to supply plausible mechanisms, and a "rational" time scheme; he did not offer new interpretations of its deepest meanings.

CHAPTER 6

The Life Force

I *Needham—A Strange But Significant Collaborator*

LATE in 1744 Portuguese fishermen of the vicinity of Lisbon came to know very well a most singular priest, a young Englishman with the large oval eyes and the heart-shaped face of a Boucher cherub, a face whose striking beauty was slightly marred by a distinctly monumental nose. The name of this spare young man in black robes, who would become within a few years one of Buffon's most important collaborators, possibly the most important, was John Turberville Needham. At this time he was a teacher of philosophy in Lisbon's Roman Catholic English college, and, although delicate health would soon oblige him to return to England, he was actively pursuing a variety of scientific interests, chiefly involving marine life, in intervals from his duties at the college.

He was seeking specimens of a very particular ocean creature. Although he could not name the creature and had himself never actually seen one, he knew almost exactly what it looked like and could describe it at length. He eventually decided that a type of squid, a calamary, was the creature he was looking for.

The fishermen, whom Needham characterized as "Persons, who are not much exposed to the Sallies of a too lively Imagination," [1] would certainly not have understood his quest. For this, one would need considerable acquaintance with the thought patterns, the basic assumptions, of the "initiates" in the use of that mysterious new instrument of scientific research, the microscope.

Almost all of the early microscopists believed that their newly discovered microscopic world differed very little from the macroscopic world that all men know. They assumed that the Creator, in fashioning the microscopic realm, had used once again essentially the same blueprints, changing only the scale, and that the minute creatures they dimly perceived through their lenses must therefore strongly resemble various large and familiar creatures in the world around them. They believed, in fact, that for almost all of these microscopic creatures there must exist a macroscopic analogue. This assumption, which may be call the Micromégas, or big-little, fallacy from Voltaire's celebrated *conte philosophique,* was stated quite explicitly by Needham in his *An Account of Some New Microscopical Discoveries* in 1745:

. . . a Drop of Water, the Diameter of which exceeds not a Line, may be a Sea, not only as daily Experience shews, in the Capacity which it has of containing, and affording Sustenance to Millions of Animals, but also in the Similitude which these very Animals may bear to several known Species in that part of the Creation, which is the Object of our naked Eyes . . . it wants not Instances to prove, that the peculiar Inhabitants of several Portions of Matter often bear a near Resemblance to each other, tho' they differ extreamly in Magnitude.[2]

In 1743, in an experiment reported to the Royal Society of London, Needham named some moving microscopic filaments, which he had observed, "eels": "upon account of their being an aquatick Animalcule not unlike the Fresh-Water Eel, with this Difference, that in them both Extremities are alike without any Appearance of Mouth or Head." [3] Similarly, in 1746 Buffon suggested that the sole microscopic plant identified at that time might be in reality, not a single species, but a miniature forest containing a vast number of distinctly different plants (H.N. II, p. 15).

This fallacy was reflected in both of the two most prominent contemporary theories of animal generation. The "ovists" held that every individual animal began in an "egg," pictured, by analogy with the eggs of certain insects and long-incubated hen's eggs, as a tiny capsule containing a replica in miniature of the adult animal, a replica presumably complete in every detail although certain features of the adult might not yet be fully developed. On the other hand, the "animalculists," opponents and denouncers of the ovists, held that the minute creatures that so greatly resembled tadpoles which Leeuwenhoek had discovered in the seminal fluid of male animals must certainly represent the first stage in the life of the individual and that the adult animal must develop from them precisely as a frog does from a tadpole. Both groups explained the inescapable influence of a second parent, the one who had not supplied, as the case might

be, either the female "egg" or the male "animalcule," through
vague references to mystic infused spirits.

It was the Micromégas fallacy, then, that guided Needham's
search along the banks of the Tagus in 1744. Abraham Trembley,
the most discussed microscopist in Europe, had recently discovered a species of microscopic creature, the freshwater polyp,
which, when cut into two sections by the experimenter, was
capable of forming new and complete individuals from each of
the severed halves. Further, a somewhat similar process of division
appeared to be its natural method of reproduction. Needham was
convinced that Trembley's remarkable polyps must have macroscopic analogues. He felt, too, that only by finding an analogue
sufficiently large to permit detailed dissection could the nature
of this strange new method of reproduction be fully explored.[4]

Needham had little difficulty in finding likely candidates to
experiment upon. First there were clusters of barnacles found on
the beach in the heat of summer, and then a large microorganism
discovered in puddles of stagnant rain water near the beach.
Finally, however, he settled on the calamary, the squid that the
fishermen of Lisbon took in nets in the shallow waters near the
mouth of the Tagus. Here at last was a sizable creature that
answered reasonably well to Trembley's description of the polyp.
Needham collected a number of specimens and began modern
science's first detailed study of the squid, with the disappointing
result that he was at length obliged to admit that they were not
really very much like microscopic polyps. Toward the end of the
year, however, the chain of experiments that had seemed so close
to total failure abruptly delivered an unexpected success, disclos-
ing to Needham's startled eye, he was certain, the macroscopic
analogue of a microorganism of far greater significance than
Trembley's polyps. In the middle of December a specimen squid
that had been patiently undergoing vivisection suddenly began
to spawn. Needham proceeded to an examination of the milt of
his male specimens: "When I first made this Discovery, I little
surmised, that a new Apparatus was forming itself for the Reception of the Semen, and therefore was much surprised to find
scattered up and down in several Parts of it spiral, elastick
Springs inclosed in a transparent cartilaginous Tube, nor could
I then imagine their Use."[5] He shortly determined that these
extremely small tubes, "which . . . exceed not an Horse-Hair in

Diameter," served as containing vessels for the milt and that the milt was ejected from them at the proper time in a markedly mechanical manner by means of the spiral springs they enclosed and a system of valves. Both the general appearance and the constant movement of the "Milt-Vessels," or spermatophores, as they are now called, convinced Needham that an observer with microscopes only slightly less powerful than his would inevitably have concluded that "this little microscopical Machine" was a living creature, rather than merely an intricate piece of protoplasmic clockwork. In the fashion of many scientists of the day, he immediately extrapolated a generalization of enormous importance from this single observation, namely, that Leeuwenhoek's spermatic "animalcules" were similarly "mechanical":

To conclude, if I had ever seen the supposed Animalcules in the Semen of any living Creature, I could perhaps be able to determine with some Certainty, whether they were really living Creatures, or might possibly be nothing more than immensely less Machines analogous to these Milt-Vessels, which may be only in Large, what these are in Miniature.[6]

Leeuwenhoek's discovery of the spermatic animalcules had completely revolutionized speculation concerning the nature of animal generation. It would seem that Needham, armed with convincing proof that many of the moving specks viewed through the microscope might be something other than living creatures, was now in a position to effect a second revolution. But he failed, puzzlingly, to make any attempt to verify these speculations, perhaps due to a refusal by his spiritual superiors to grant the necessary permission to perform the experiments. Once he had returned to England he was able to be present, in the house of his friend John Hill, during microscopic observations of the seminal fluid of a dog, and he, and others present, became convinced that the movements of the animalcules were not, in fact, caused by the activity of their "tails," as had always been assumed. Here, however, he was apparently willing to let the matter rest. He was similarly neglectful of his important earlier discovery that the pollen of certain plants will eject "a Train of Globules" immediately after they are moistened with a drop of water, contenting himself with the observation: "The Analogy between the Vegetable and Animal World in this Particular will appear to be still greater than has been hitherto imagined, as the Nature of the *Farina faecundans*, and its Action upon the Application of Water, not unlike that of the Milt-Vessels mentioned above, imply something of a similar Mechanism within the globules contrived for the same Purpose." [7]

At this time Needham was widely respected for his extraordinary skill in the use of the microscope, but he had not yet manifested the facility in developing remarkably abstruse general theoretical systems for which he would be famed throughout Europe within a few decades. This facet of the talent of the young professor of sacred philosophy would make its appearance only after the short period of his active collaboration with Buffon.

II   *Meanwhile, Back at the Ranch: Buffon's First Speculations on Biological Reproduction*

When Buffon first turned his attention to the sciences of life in the early 1740's he quickly concentrated his efforts upon a single problem: the elaboration of a viable theory of generation. The ability to reproduce its own kind, whereby every individual mortal creature acquires a dimension in eternity, had long been a subject for speculation, but, with regard to the precise mechanism of the miracle, the actual processes involved, science had as yet advanced no theory that was not obviously (sometimes preposterously) inadequate. Man's very ability to understand nature seemed at issue in this supreme riddle, and Buffon rose to meet the challenge with something very like awe:

> . . . it is not in the individual that one encounters the greatest marvel, it is in the succession, in the renewal and in the persistence of the species that Nature appears totally inconceivable. This capacity to reproduce its own kind, which animals and plants alike possess, this type of unity that subsists forever and appears eternal, this procreative virtue that is exercised in perpetuity without ever nearing destruction, is for us a mystery whose final depths, it seems, we shall never be permitted to sound. (H.N. II, p. 3)

It was an area in which the thoughts of "scientists" tended to blend ominously into those of frank metaphysicians. Buffon was fully aware of the tenuousness of science's hold on this problem, and he felt a need, here, for some very basic changes in scientific

procedures. The role of science, he had always insisted, was not to
concern itself with *why*, only with *how*, with the means by which
the events and phenomena of nature are effected. Now, he suggested, the question might better be "how might?":

. . . what then are the hidden means which Nature might possibly
employ in the reproduction of creatures? . . . This question, which is
the only valid one . . . permits us to construct hypotheses and to select from among them the one that appears to us to bear the greatest
analogy to the other phenomena of Nature . . . if we do not succeed
in explaining the mechanism by which Nature accomplishes reproduction, we shall at least arrive at something that has more the appearance
of truth than anything that has thus far been proposed. (H.N. II,
pp. 32–4)

He thus clearly separated himself not only from those of his
colleagues who perversely meddled with the *why* of the mystery
by invoking "final causes," a device he regarded as little more
than the willful confusing of cause and effect, but also from the
patient researchers, typified by the young Needham, who were
exclusively concerned with adding to the purely factual data.
Buffon was convinced that the available published data was already sufficient to permit meaningful theoretical formulations,
and he devoted years to mastering it. References to his reading
in the field occur in his correspondence as early as February,
1739.[8]

The review of the literature of biological generation that he
published in the second volume of the *Histoire Naturelle* in 1749
included descriptions and comments on the work of a few great
anatomists, such as Harvey, Valisnieri, Graaf, and Malpighi, and
a concerted attack upon the doctrine of preformationism. To a
large extent, both the ovists and the animalculists, the two dominant schools among the theorists, were preformationists. The
seeds of many plants and the eggs of some insects, as noted
above, contain what appear, superficially, to be minute replicas
of the mature individual, and the preformationists assumed that
that was precisely what they did contain: infinitesimal replicas
of the adult, complete in every detail, even to the presence in
their miniature gonads of even more minute replicas of themselves, which in turn contained. . . . An ultimate consequence
of the preformationist doctrine, pushed to the limits of absurdity,

and Buffon—the better to demonstrate its implausibility—did not
hesitate to push it at least that far, was the belief that within the
body of either Adam or Eve, according to whether the preformationist happened to be an ovist or an animalculist, there had been
contained, in an almost infinite progression of reduced scales, the
totality of all the human bodies that were to exist on earth from
the Creation to the Day of Judgment. Buffon assaulted the theory
with mathematical analysis: "A man would be as large in relation
to the sixth-generation seed as the entire universe is in relation
to the tiniest speck of matter that can be made out through a
microscope," and with blunt common sense: "One asks how a
living creature can produce a replica of itself, and they reply that
the answer is that the replica was already produced. Are we to
accept that as a solution?" (H.N. II, pp. 28, 156).

Buffon strongly favored epigenesis, the rival doctrine, whose
supporters held that the embryo is actually formed at the time of
impregnation, as the end result of a process involving the assembling of its constituent parts. Only epigenesis, Buffon felt, could
satisfactorily explain monstrous births, cases in which the reproductive process has gone awry, such as the stillborn calf he himself had displayed before the Académie Royale des Sciences in
1744. And only epigenesis could explain the piecemeal nature of
the resemblance the offspring bears to both parents, in evidence,
he noted, whenever one is led to remark that a child has "its
father's eyes and its mother's mouth" (H.N. II, p. 68), and most
particularly in evidence in the cases of hybrid animals like the
mule and in people of mixed race.

He suggested, in his preliminary historical overview, that earlier
theorists had erred primarily in artificially limiting the scope of
the problem. The Cartesians, for example, were determined to
see in all phenomena only the varied aspects of matter in motion,
and failed to recognize the complex nature of matter itself, re-
fusing to admit the existence within matter of obscure forces
whose effects cannot always be visually demonstrated: "Instead
of an effort to determine the nature of these forces . . . there has
been an effort to banish them from philosophy; they have nevertheless reappeared, with unexampled brilliance, in the form of
gravitation, chemical affinities, electrical phenomena, etc." (H.N.
II, p. 486). The key to the solution, he felt, must lie among these
"obscure forces." He criticized too his predecessors' general tend-

ency to attack the problem at the top rather than from the bottom, that is, to attempt to explain only sexual generation, considered in isolation, and to ignore such related, and obviously more basic phenomena as the asexual reproduction of polyps, by a simple process of division, and the growth of certain trees from cuttings.

Having established the need for a strong stand against any narrow limiting of the problem, Buffon proceeded to add to the fundamental "givens" an assumed connection between nutrition and generation, thus making an explanation of the processes of nutrition and growth the inevitable point of departure for any theory of reproduction.

Animals, Buffon observed, can obtain nourishment only from the bodies of plants or other animals, and plants too seem to require that the soil around them contain some remnants of living things. Animals, moreover, are able to retain only a portion of the material they consume. From these facts one might conclude that the portion of the nourishment that is not rejected is, in some way, of the same nature as some of the material that makes up the animal's body. Buffon, however, was not content with any such limited conclusion as this. As the body of one living creature may be reduced to minute particles and these particles may become a part of the body of another creature, there must be, he reasoned, one single, divisible substance out of which the bodies of all living things, animal and plant alike, are formed. And, as the particles into which this substance divides, these "organic molecules," can sometimes be shaped into a living creature simply by bringing them together, to judge from well-known instances of spontaneous generation, some elemental form of life must actually reside in each one of the particles. Life itself, then, must be regarded as nothing other than "a physical property of matter" (H.N. II, p. 17), probably closely akin to gravitation, magnetism, electricity, and "chemical affinity."

A conclusion this broad can be considered inductive only in a very loose sense, and, once Buffon had distinguished his "organic molecules" from the "particles of brute matter," there would seem to have remained very little to prevent him from expatiating freely on the nature of the organic molecules. He preferred, though, to regard his logic, however freewheeling it might be, as basically inductive, and he limited his description of the organic molecules to the specifying of only a few qualities. He had assumed that there is only one, universal organic matter, common to all plants and animals, only one type of organic molecule, and he was therefore obliged, by the very diversity of human forms, to assume further that the organic molecules were plastic and could be molded, temporarily, into a wide variety of forms. As these molecules were, by definition, "alive," they must therefore be assumed to have characteristic patterns of movement, and their adaptability and variety had to be extended to include this movement.

Buffon also stated, in the earliest version of the theory, that the number of organic molecules was fixed, and that they were in the normal course of events neither created nor destroyed (H.N. II, p. 44). If this were not the case, if every act of reproduction could directly increase the numbers of organic molecules, within little more than a century, he calculated, selecting a convenient example, a single elm seed could give rise to a quantity of wood equal in bulk to the earth itself. The simplest method of containing this awesome reproductive power—and Buffon never hesitated to impute to Nature a constant preference for simplicity in the means it employed—must be a fixed limitation set upon the amount of building material available. The assumption that the quantity of organic molecules in circulation remained relatively stable introduced into the natural scheme of things a certain fitness and order, and closed off an abyss of disturbing possibilities, and on this basis alone it became a part of the theory.

Having assumed, then, that organic molecules may not be manufactured but that they do occur in a great variety of temporary forms, and having observed that living bodies, both plant and animal, absorb and assimilate organic molecules from a great many sources, Buffon concluded that each living body, every living creature, must possess the power to reshape the molecules and transform their patterns of activity to whatever extent this might be necessary in order to adapt them to its own purposes. In fact, each organ of every living body must possess such power. Confronted with the need for a new label, Buffon gave this remarkable assimilating power the deliberately equivocal name of *moule intérieur,* which may be translated as *interior mold* or, better, *interior molding force.* The only efforts he made to describe the *moule intérieur* took the form of comparisons with gravitation and matter's other "obscure forces." However, despite his obvious desire to confer an aura Newtonism on the *moule*, in the details of his theorizing it often seemed to have more in common with Plato's archetypes and Aristotle's forms than with Newton's gravitation. The *moule* of an individual creature, which was a sort of composite of the *moules* of all of its organs, was itself merely a particular exemplar of the *moule* of a species. The original exemplar of the *moule* of a species, Buffon was willing to concede, possibly for want of a better explanation, must have come into existence at the time of the Creation (H.N. II, p. 426).

Thus, by the logic of his own theory, grounded in a simplistic view of nature, Buffon, who had in one of his earliest scientific quarrels denounced the neat categories of Linnaeus' systematic taxonomy as figments of the imagination (H.N. I, pp. 37–40), was obliged to regard the notion of the species as a fact of nature. But he was able to provide a more direct factual basis for this conclusion, seemingly at so far a remove from the inductive origins of his chain of reasoning. He proposed that individual creatures, however different they might be in appearance, be regarded as belonging to the same species if they were capable of producing together a fertile offspring; mules would be held as the classic example of sterile offspring. This "working" definition of species was long associated with his name, although some historians of science have seen in it chiefly an unacknowledged borrowing from John Ray. It was a definition that lent itself readily to experimental verification, and it thus conferred upon *species* a degree of "reality" then enjoyed by none of the other taxonomic categories, whose value was generally felt to be largely heuristic. And, this happy juxtaposition of the practical and the theoretical, the intersecting of a theoretical extension with established practice in determining the limits of a species, appeared to lend a limited kind of "reality" to the theory itself.

The *moule*'s role as the theoretical basis for the concept of species, however, was remote from the first functions Buffon assigned to it. The unceasing activity of this internal shaping force was first apparent in the individual plant or animal's growth and development through nutrition. During the processes of nutrition the food taken into the body was reduced to an agglomerate of organic molecules and particles of brute matter. All those that could not be assimilated were quickly eliminated from the body, while those that remained circulated throughout their new host, penetrating to every organ. The *moule* of each organ of the body was continuously employed in impressing upon the newly arrived organic molecules the form and pattern of activity appropriate to that organ. When all the organs of the body had, in the course of time, reached a certain size they would abruptly lose their "ductility," their capacity of further expansion, though the activity of the *moules* themselves would not be interrupted.

Since generation customarily made its appearance at the very time that growth and development came to an end, at puberty, Buffon concluded that the new process was simply a continuation of the earlier process, utilizing the same means to a different end. Organic molecules, then, continued to find their way to the various organs of the body, and they continued to undergo a variety of specializing temporary transformations as they came within the spheres of influence of the *moules* of the organs, but, as there was now no longer any place for them within the organs, they were unceremoniously ejected from them once their transformation had been completed. In time all of these reshaped and rejected organic molecules found their way to a central reservoir within the body, and this reservoir was none other than the body's organ of generation. Once gathered together, and freed from the constraining power of the *moules,* these living and moving molecules, each one endowed with a form and a pattern of activity characteristic of one of the host body's organs, would, Buffon felt, inevitably tend to group themselves in such a way as to form a miniature replica of the host body. And thus the mysterious *moules* would in effect have reproduced themselves, inside the body. Although Buffon never formally reduced the theory to this degree of simplicity, he apparently visualized the *moules* themselves as nothing more than the cumulative action of the distinctive molecules that made up each organ, on the theory that a malleable molecule tossed into, for example, a mass of bobbing and quivering triangles must quickly become another bobbing and quivering triangle.

Pushed thus far, then, Buffon's theory of organic molecules and *moules* appeared to provide an explanation of the mechanism of asexual generation. In the extension of the theory to include sexual generation, however, the very facility of the earlier explanations became a source of difficulty, posing the unwelcome question: If the assembled excess molecules tend to shape themselves into an embryo automatically, with the faster and lighter ones moving to the edges and the heavier and slower ones to the centers, or in accord with some roughly similar process, why do not all creatures reproduce asexually, by parthenogenesis, as Charles Bonnet had demonstrated that aphids do? Buffon considered a number of possible answers and finally selected the one that, because of its extreme simplicity, appeared to him to be the most "natural." In the higher and more complex organisms, those that reproduced by sexual generation, the superfluous organic molecules collected in the organs of generation were in a state of extreme agitation, each one moving far too rapidly and violently to be able to assume a position in any permanent structure. When, however, the excess organic molecules, that is, the seminal fluids, of a male were mixed with those of a female, organic molecules that had been shaped by a particular organ in one parent would tend to collide constantly with the molecules shaped by the same organ in the other parent, since their patterns of movement, although highly complex, would be almost identical. As a result of these constant collisions, the molecules that represented a particular organ in each of the two seminal fluids, male and female, that had been mixed together would tend to interfere with one another's movements, to slow one another, to form combinations, and these heavy combinations would soon diminish the degree of agitation in the mixed seminal fluids to a point at which the permanent structure of the embryo would be able to emerge. The molecules shaped by the organs of generation in the most vigorous of the two parents would constitute the central point about which the other molecules, now linked in disparate pairs, would group themselves. In viviparous animals, of course, the entire process would be able to proceed only in an environment in which the tenuous existence of the newly formed embryo could be assured on more than a momentary basis, that is, in the womb of the female (H.N. II, pp. 334–65).

Viewed in its entirety, Buffon's theory of generation suggests that if he had turned his literary talents to more conventional genres he might have displayed an uncommon mastery of intricate plot structure. It is a singularly attractive neoclassical edifice, possessing all the beauty that flows from simplicity and order, but, of course, it stood in much the same relation to nature as the formal, terraced gardens of his estate at Montbard did to the shaggy forests that covered the neighboring hills. We no longer accept simplicity as a mark of conformity to Nature's plan, and it surprises us that serious scientists ever did. Nevertheless, the theory was widely respected for a very long time. In 1770, an account of Buffon's system completely dominated the general review of the various contemporary systems of generation in the article "Generation" of the first edition of the *Encyclopaedia Britannica,* whose general editor and principal author, William Smellie, was later to be the most important English translator of Buffon's work. Almost a century later, Charles Darwin, attempting to formulate a workable theory of generation, still an unsolved problem, submitted his views in manuscript to T. H. Huxley, who promptly advised him to compare his system with Buffon's before considering publication. Darwin procured a copy of Buffon, and shortly replied:

I have read Buffon: whole pages are laughably like mine. It is surprising how candid it makes one to see one's view in another man's words. I am rather ashamed of the whole affair, but not converted to a no-belief. What a kindness you have done me with your "vulpine sharpness." [9]

The theory was not, of course, totally original with Buffon. In citing the *Vénus Physique* of his friend Maupertuis, Buffon acknowledged that "one will find in this treatise general views that differ very little from those I have set forth" (H.N. I, p. 164), and, in 1769, John Turberville Needham pointed out certain similarities between the Buffonian theory, as he understood it, and Bacon's thoughts on generation.[10]

In appraising the theory, it must be remembered that most of the sciences to which we owe our present understanding of the process of generation, such as chemistry, histology, genetics, and the like were in Buffon's time either in their earliest infancy or not yet in existence. Even the anatomists had yet to put their house in order. If a physician were to attempt today to explain the functioning of the genes and the formation of the zygote in a highly simplified way to an intelligent child, one totally ignorant of even the most basic concepts of chemistry, with no knowledge whatsoever of the structure of the cell, and with only the fuzziest notions of microorganisms, his explanation would inevitably bear a strong resemblance to Buffon's system. The theory of the organic molecules was very probably as good a system as could be constructed from the data then available. Buffon himself was well aware of its shortcomings. He felt, for instance, that an entirely new branch of mathematics would have to be developed before the bisymmetrical arrangement of the molecules that made up the new embryo could be fully understood (H.N. II, p. 373).

Buffon failed at first, however, to show any interest in the experimental verification of the theory, and had apparently no plans to undertake the chain of experiments that would have to be performed if he wished to convert his chain of hypotheses into something more than a purely theoretical construction. He seemed content that his system should remain, indefinitely, nothing more than an explanation of how generation might take place. He wrote an account of his theory, dated it February 6, 1746, and set it aside for eventual inclusion in the *Histoire Naturelle*. This indifference is particularly difficult to understand in view of the fact that many of his conclusions would have lent themselves quite readily to experimental verification.

If Buffon's assumptions were justified, his conclusions correct, the male seminal fluid would be simply a collection of organic molecules, in which no permanent structure of any kind would be distinguishable, and a female seminal fluid, also an aggregate of organic molecules, identical in appearance to that of the male, would be contained in an organ located somewhere in the immediate vicinity of the womb. His principal tasks were thus, first, to demonstrate conclusively that Leeuwenhoek's spermatic animalcules were simply temporary forms resulting from chance combinations of organic molecules, and not animals at all, and, second, to find and identify the female's seminal fluid. All of the necessary experiments, however, involved the use of the microscope, and that still crude instrument could be used with complete success only by a mere handful of skilled and clever men. In a letter to Jean Jalabert of August 2, 1745, Buffon had briefly described some experiments he had performed on the reproductive organs of plants in which he had used a microscope. His chief impression seems to have been that the microscope had not yet been sufficiently developed to be of any real service to science.

Perhaps, too, he felt some hesitancy in moving a theory that covered so much ground out of the realm of pure speculation. In

committing himself to it, even tentatively, he had entered a theoretical blind alley, but so long as the theory lacked experimental
verification, he could not be said to have walled up the entranceway behind him. That final, fateful step would be taken only after
he had met John Turberville Needham.

III *The Buffon-Needham Collaboration*

One might assume that any contemporary work that presented
evidence in support of his adventurous theory would have greatly
impressed Buffon—such a work, for example, as the account of
John Needham's early experiments that was published in 1745, a
work that specifically challenged the assumption that Leeuwenhoek's spermatic animalcules were indeed minute animals. But
this was not the case. Needham's work was cited in the earliest,
purely theoretical section of Buffon's writings on generation, dated
1746, but only in connection with the evidence advanced in support of the assumption that nutrition and generation were simply
different aspects of a single bodily process. The fact that Needham's squid had spawned only after the winter's cold had drastically reduced their bodily activities, and consequently their need
for food, appeared to Buffon to demonstrate a direct connection
between nutrition and the reproductory processes, and it was
placed in the balance next to such similarly significant items as
the chubbiness of eunuchs and the proved efficacy of fasting in
reducing sexual desire (H.N. II, pp. 71, 72).

Buffon's first meetings with Needham also apparently failed to
produce any very definite impressions. Needham was an expatriate, more continental than English by education, a common
fate for English Roman Catholic clergy in the eighteenth century.
He had been sent to France for the first time at the age of nine,
to the English college at Douai, and he had remained there, with
only occasional visits to England, for eighteen years. In 1738 he
had been ordained a priest at Cambrai. His true homeland was a
series of encapsulated English Roman Catholic communities set
down in various French cities. Thus, very shortly after his return
from Portugal, he had left England once again, for Paris. During
his brief stay in England, however, Needham had made a strongly
favorable impression on Martin Folkes, the President of the Royal
Society, who had long been in correspondence with Buffon, and

he carried with him to Paris Folkes's earnest recommendations to Buffon. On July 4, 1746, Needham wrote a long, formal "letter" to Folkes, for inclusion in the *Philosophical Transactions* of the Royal Society, touching briefly on his newly established relations with Buffon in the course of a description of a series of experiments with electricity which he had witnessed in Paris:

. . . at least, this is my present Thought of the Matter; and I am the more confident in advancing it, since that I have learnt your Friend Monsieur *de Buffon* is of the same Opinion, for whose Judgment I have the greatest Deference. I remember he told me one Day, when I had the Honour of waiting upon him, that he thought the whole Subject of Electricity, though illustrated with so great a variety of Experiments, very far from being yet sufficiently ripe for the Establishment of a Course of Laws, or indeed of any certain one, fixed and determined in all its Circumstances. . . .[11]

Needham's unfailing humility had evidently led Buffon to regard him at first encounter more in the light of a student than a possible colleague.

Shortly thereafter, however, Buffon altered his opinion. On January 22, 1747, Needham was elected to the Royal Society of London, at the age of thirty-three, the first English Roman Catholic priest to be so honored, and this may well have impressed Buffon, always sensitive to gradations in rank. The more immediate cause of the change, however, was undoubtedly Buffon's first close look at Needham's microscope, which was far superior to any he had ever used, or even seen. It made possible magnifications of better than four hundred diameters with remarkable clarity, a degree of magnification which Buffon considered fully adequate to bring the organic molecules themselves into view (H.N. II, p. 255). With such an instrument, and with an assistant like the virtuoso Abbé Needham, the experiments that were required to confirm his theory of generation, which he had at first regarded as forbiddingly difficult, would be, Buffon apparently concluded, almost ludicrously simple. And, in the early months of 1748, these experiments were under way.

Examination of fluid taken from a Graafian follicle of a female dog yielded immediate and spectacular results, jubilantly reported by Buffon:

I therefore examined this fluid under the microscope, and, at my very first glance, I had the satisfaction of seeing in it moving bodies with tails that were almost exactly the same as those I had just seen in the seminal fluid of the male dog. Mr. Needham and M. Daubenton, who examined the specimen after I had finished were so surprised at this resemblance that they were unable to persuade themselves that these spermatic animals were not in fact those of the male dog that we had just observed; they thought that I must have forgotten to change the object-slide . . . consequently, Mr. Needham himself took another object-slide, and another toothpick, and, having personally collected some of the fluid from the incision in the follicle, he examined it first, and saw once again the same animals, the same moving bodies, and he too was convinced, as I was. . . . (H.N. II, p. 203)

This was the vital first step: the demonstration that the female produced a "spermatic fluid" precisely identical in appearance to that of the male. Buffon's account of the experiment, skillfully and meticulously conducted and leading straight to monumental error, is still disturbing, an uncomfortable mystery. Erik Nordenskiöld, a modern historian of biology, attempted an explanation: "What Buffon and his collaborators . . . actually saw in the follicular fluid it is difficult to say; perhaps detached cells from the follicular epithelium; maybe also coagulation products." [12]

Persuaded almost immediately that his theories had stood the test of experimentation, Buffon was not of a mind to tarry long at these uncongenial tasks. Within a few short months he was able to complete, to his own satisfaction, the entire series of experiments, to deposit with the secretary of the Académie Royale des Sciences a sealed document dated May 17, 1748, that briefly summarized his many discoveries, and to leave Paris for Montbard in accord with his normal spring schedule. He left the tedious and routine rechecking that needed to be done to his industrious English friend, the Abbé Needham.

IV   *Needham's Parallel Theory*

At several points in the second volume of the *Histoire Naturelle* Buffon referred to "experiments connected with my theory which Mr. Needham has kindly consented to perform" (H.N. II, p. 184). These included almost all of those that involved the reduction of animal and vegetable matter, through cooking, soaking, and mashing, to simple collections of organic molecules. Needham's willing cooperation relieved Buffon, he felt, of even the necessity of describing this section of the chain of experiments: "but it is pointless to enter into further detail here concerning my observations on plant infusions, for Mr. Needham has followed the development of these experiments with much more care than I would have been able to devote to them myself, and that skilled naturalist will very shortly publish his findings in this area . . . and I must confess that the ideas I communicated to him on this subject have yielded a finer harvest in his hands than they could have in my own . . ." (H.N. II, p. 256). In effect, then, Buffon's departure for Montbard ended the collaboration.

To Needham, continuing the work alone, the movements his microscope uncovered in the infusions, these disparate and grainy masses of organic jelly, soon became objects of intense fascination: "It was visible, that the Motion, tho' it had then no one Characteristic of Spontaneity, yet sprung from an Effort of something teeming as it were within the Particle, and not from any Fermentation in the Liquid, or other extraneous Cause." [13] He was convinced that he was actually observing the life force at work in its most elemental form:

. . . I had at this time certain Proofs of it; tho' not so plain and incontestable as those I procur'd a few Days before Mr. *de Buffon* left *Paris* for the Country, and which I prosecuted after his Departure. These I communicated to him in few Words the Night before he began his Journey, yet he was not at that time acquainted with any special Detail of the many Singularities that attend these latter Vegetations, for I had but just then made and enter'd upon the Discovery of them myself.[14]

These experiments, so cavalierly dismissed by Buffon, were to launch Needham into a prolonged effort, lasting some thirty years, to elaborate a theoretical system of his own, one that would attempt a reconciliation of theology and biology. His theory closely paralleled Buffon's idea of *moules* and was doubtless directly inspired by it, but Needham did not share Buffon's aversion to mixing together scientific and metaphysical notions, and his own system was a strange addition of apples and oranges.

Needham's comments, at different times, on his indebtedness to Buffon's theory varied widely. In 1769, in a reply to Lazzaro Spallanzani and several other eminent microscopists who had

attacked either his own or Buffon's published accounts of the
experiments performed in 1748, Needham stated that his own
theories could not properly be distinguished from Buffon's and
that those who pretended to detect some differences between the
two were mistaken: the theories were essentially identical, and,
furthermore, he and Buffon had performed together the experiments on which the theories had been based.[15] In a work published in 1776, however, he affirmed the total independence of his
theory from all other contemporary theories, having been driven
to this extreme, as his friend Archibald MacLaine remarked in
the British *Monthly Review,* by "a press-gang of materialists, who
wanted to force him into their service." [16] In 1784, after Needham's death, MacLaine commented further on the singular anom-
aly of Needham's role in the Enlightenment: "this honest man was
narrow, even to superstition and bigotry, in his religious system;
and we never knew a man in whom there was such an unaccount-
able mixture of implicit faith and philosophical curiosity as Mr.
Needham." [17] Needham's theological concerns are constantly reflected in his terminology, and they tend to mask the resemblance
of his ideas to Buffon's, though at times the terms he used were
more Buffonian than metaphysical—as when, for instance, he
spoke of "a kind of universal *Semen*" that is "moulded into other
Bodies." [18] Further masking was contributed by Needham's endless rehashing of his theory through a long series of separate
works, some in English and some in French, restatements that
gradually accumulated into a formidable obstacle to comprehen-
sion. The reader is constantly being advised by Needham that the
work he has before him is not the final exposition of a definitive
theory but merely an "imperfect sketch" of a theory that is rapidly
approaching its final form, but has not yet done so.[19] And, on
occasion, Needham suggests to his reader that the particular work
at hand has been so badly written that he must not hope to understand it until he has read it through at least twice,[20] and, certainly, few readers would care to argue the point. Even the Abbé
Mann, Needham's devoted protégé and biographer, could only
deplore the quality of Needham's published work:

. . . his philosophical views were presented to the public exactly as
they had first presented themselves in his thoughts, without method
and without order. In speaking and in writing, he almost invariably

failed to convey a true impression of the extent and depth of his knowledge. I have often tried to persuade him to recast his works, to reduce them to an orderly system contained within a single volume, and to publish a complete edition of everything that merited preservation: I offered to assist him in the work, but my efforts were unavailing: he confessed that it demanded a greater effort on his part to put his ideas in order and to present them in a systematic manner than it did to produce them.[21]

Needham's version of the theory had begun to take shape in his mind during the spring and summer of 1748:

My first Proofs therefore were drawn from a close Attendance to all the common Infusions, particularly that of Wheat pounded in a marble Mortar . . . after some time allow'd to the Water to call off the Salts and volatile Parts . . . the Substance became softer, more divided, and more attenuated: To the naked Eye, or to the Touch, it appear'd a gelatinous Matter, but in the Microscope was seen to consist of innumerable Filaments; and then it was that the Substance was in its highest Point of Exaltation, just breaking, as I may say, into Life. These Filaments would swell from an interior Force so active, and so productive, that even before they resolved into, or shed any moving Globules, they were perfect Zoophytes teeming with Life, and Self-moving.[22]

Needham witnessed this process of "spontaneous generation" of microorganisms in more than eighty infusions, and under a variety of conditions,[23] though he was careful never to "torture his experiments in order to wrest perjured testimony from them," as he was to accuse his friend Lazzaro Spallanzani of doing. He believed that Spallanzani's results, apparently disproving spontaneous generation, differed from his only because the Italian microscopist had heated his infusions too drastically, thus destroying the life force within them.[24]

Convinced by the evidence, accepting fully Buffon's conclusion that life, the capacity to arrange itself spontaneously into living organisms, must be numbered among the basic properties of matter, Needham attempted to expand the theory into a more general explanation of the nature of matter itself. He took as his point of departure a suggestion of Sir Isaac Newton's that matter, like light, might be broken down into a number of simpler components.[25] On the basis of his experiments, assisted by metaphysical training, Needham felt he could identify the main components as two simple "principles," which lacked extension in space and were therefore not divisible themselves, but which, acting in concert, could form the divisible compound known as matter.[26]

One of the two principles was referred to fairly consistently throughout his works as "*la force résistante,*" but the other is given many labels: "*la force productrice,*" "*la force végétative,*" "*l'agent moteur,*" "*l'activité motrice,*" and "*le principe de vitalité matériel.*" The most convenient terms are, perhaps, simply "the active force" and "the resisting force." These two forces were seldom in exact balance, and the different qualities of the many known types of matter could be explained as manifestations of the specific degree to which one of the forces predominated over the other. In the matter that composed a living body, for instance, the active force was almost totally unopposed by the resisting force. In soluble salts or any corrosive substance that had a destructive effect on living flesh the resisting force could be assumed to be definitely in the ascendant.[27] Spontaneous generation resulted from a readjustment of the principles. Soaking or boiling material that had once been part of a living body would gradually remove the soluble salts, or related substances, in which the resisting force was particularly strong, so that the active force could slowly regain its earlier position of dominance.

Theological difficulties paralyzed the theory at this point. Needham insisted that the microorganisms that appeared in the infusions—some of which he called "eels," a term he seems to have been particularly fond of—were not truly "alive." They were endowed, not with life itself, but merely with an elemental form of life, a kind of prelife, which he called "*vitalité.*" Since these microscopic eels, these "*êtres vitaux,*" were able to reproduce by a simple process of division, he argued, they could not possibly possess sensitivity or intelligence, because these are indivisible simple principles that can be bestowed only by God.[28] And, in order to satisfy any lingering doubts the reader, or censor, might have in regard to the distinction between *êtres vitaux* and *êtres vivants,* Needham noted that, in addition to *vitalité,* the active principle could manifest itself as electricity, gravitation, magnetism or chemical affinity.[29]

"In Nature," Buffon had stated, very early in the presentation of his own theory, "the abstract does not exist; there are no simple principles, all is compound; we shall never penetrate to the inmost structure of things" (H.N. II, p. 22). Buffon may have believed, with Needham, that the microscope permitted the human eye to penetrate to the very threshold of the ideal, and perhaps beyond, but a salutary caution prevented him from explicitly saying so.

V Aftermath: Voltaire's Attacks

Needham's theories brought him both fame and ignominy, in almost equal measure. In January, 1765, in Turin, Italy, James Boswell made Needham's acquaintance, noting:

> I called this morning on Gray, who lives at the Academy. I found there Mr. Needham of the Royal Society, whose acquaintance I much wished for. When I hear of such a man's being in a place where I arrive at, I go immediately and make him the first visit, although I stand upon the very pinnacle of punctilios with the British in general. I found him a learned, accurate, easy man.[30]

A decade later, however, in 1775, Boswell referred in passing to Needham, in a private letter, as "Honest Tub," a center of "merriment."[31] Needham had temporarily become a figure of fun to much of the world as a result of a polemic he had engaged in with Voltaire.

In 1765 in Geneva Needham had published several thin pamphlets intended as rebuttals to Voltaire's *Lettres sur les Miracles*. Voltaire's reaction was horrendous, out of all proportion to the provocation. He first constructed, figuratively speaking, a persona, an ideal recipient for Voltaire's satire, shaped to order, which he named Needham, adjusting a number of factual details in the process. The "Needham" that is subjected to endless abuse through a long series of Voltaire's pamphlets is a frenzied, hysterical Irish zealot, a shameless charlatan who pretends to create eels by sprinkling holy water on spoiled flour, and skulks about Europe "disguised as a man," acting always as an underground agent for various sinister Jesuit conspiracies. Voltaire often centered tiny bits of fiction around his persona: the "eel-priest," passing through Neufchâtel, is unmasked as a dangerous lunatic and is stoned from the gates of the city;[32] at Spa, the "eel-priest," in a company of gentlemen, launches himself into a venomous diatribe against the Protestants, calling for new and greater massacres in defense of the Faith, and is abruptly interrupted: "There was an Englishman there who had neither spoken nor laughed; he took in at a glance little Needham's face, with an air of astonishment and scorn, mixed with some anger, and said to him in English: 'Do you come from Bedlam, you booby!' " [33]

Voltaire's sustained campaign against Needham gives, at first glance, the impression of a man determinedly hunting small game with cannon. To most contemporary readers, however, Needham's name was inextricably linked to Buffon's; the frail cleric seemed to be little more than a sort of priestly English alter ego of the famed French naturalist, and the Voltaire-Needham quarrel was generally seen as a small episode in a larger Voltaire-Buffon quarrel. Buffon himself, in a letter of March 7, 1768, to the Président de Brosses, another of Voltaire's many favorite targets, echoed this view:

As I never read Voltaire's foolish trifles, it is only through my friends that I have learned of the wretched things that he has been trying to say about me; I forgive him for it, seeing it as the effect of a metaphysical malady that afflicts only his wits, and that takes its origin in an association of ideas that has linked Needham to Buffon in his mind.[34]

At the commencement of Buffon's career Voltaire had welcomed the younger man, his junior by some thirteen years, as an ally in his own campaigns against the Cartesians, as a fellow Newtonian and Anglophile, but, when it became increasingly apparent that Buffon's ambitions were on much the same scale as Voltaire's, the relationship cooled perceptibly. Then, in 1749, in the first volume of the *Histoire Naturelle,* Buffon held up to general ridicule an anonymous Italian treatise on fossils, unaware, he later protested, that its author was none other than Voltaire. The overwhelming bitterness of Voltaire, always extraordinarily sensitive to any criticism of his scientific efforts, was painfully apparent whenever he wrote of the incident, even after the passage of many years:

When I read, forty years ago, that shells from the shores of Syria had been found in the Alps, I said, I confess, in rather a bantering tone, that those shells had apparently been brought there by pilgrims returning from Jerusalem. M. de Buffon admonished me rather sharply for this in his *Théorie de la Terre,* page 281. I didn't want to quarrel with him over a few shells, but I have held to my opinion, because I believe that the impossibility of the sea's having formed the mountains has been fully demonstrated.[35]

Neither man was willing to acknowledge publicly that he was at odds with a fellow *philosophe:* both maintained the fiction of a warm mutual regard which was completely undisturbed by minor differences of opinion; but, by 1774, the nonexistent quarrel had become so heated that mutual friends were making major efforts to effect a reconciliation.

There is convincing evidence that Voltaire found the existence of Needham's theory, so vulnerable and at the same time so strangely parallel to Buffon's, a convenient vehicle for mounting attacks upon his former ally. In almost all of Voltaire's pieces in which Needham's connection with Buffon is more or less openly hinted at, there appears as well a second Buffonian surrogate: the much ridiculed French cosmogonist Benoît de Maillet. A number of the early critics of Buffon's *Théorie de la Terre* had seized upon some superficial points of resemblance between Buffon's conservative theory and de Maillet's often fantastic and always extravagantly imaginative system, even going so far as to suggest that the two cosmogonies were virtually identical. Voltaire, in adding a second bizarre personage to his satires, was simply expanding the device to include both of the two great areas of science in which Buffon had proposed major original theoretical systems. Without being obliged to mention Buffon by name, Voltaire was thus able to attack, within a single framework, both the Buffonian cosmogony and the Buffonian theory of organic molecules. Few knowledgeable readers would have been at a loss to supply the name of Buffon in, for example, Voltaire's *"Dissertation du Physicien de Saint-Flour"* of 1768: "The same physicist who, in spite of his vast erudition, adopted Needham's eels, was taken in yet again by De Maillet's mountains. . . . "[36] It seems highly probable, then, that Needham owed both his fame and the savage onslaughts of Voltaire to his brief association with Buffon. In any event, the tendency to spin theories, which was a factor in both, manifested itself in Needham's work only after 1748.

However, although Voltaire's satires demolished Needham's

reputation in the republic of letters, they did little real damage to his career. Needham moved in circles in which the enmity of Voltaire could prove an asset. In 1768 Needham received an invitation from the government of the Austrian Netherlands to come to Brussels to aid in the formation of a new scientific academy. In 1773, when the society he helped to found became the Académie Impériale et Royale des Sciences et Belles-Lettres de Bruxelles, Needham became its first director, a post he held until shortly before his death. In recognition of distinguished services he was also appointed to a canonry in the collegiate church of Dendermonde. Thus, by a strange reversal of fortune, in the last years of his life Needham rose to a position of worldly honor comparable to Buffon's and enjoyed, like Buffon, an unlimited opportunity to publish the results of his scientific labors. He contributed to the early volumes of memoirs of the Académie Impériale et Royale essays on soil reclamation, lighthouse construction, diseases of horned cattle, methods of stabilizing compass needles, the social orders of the ants and the bees, and the relative efficacy of lightning rods and prayer as defenses against lightning.

For Needham, then, the aftereffects of collaboration with Buffon were decidedly mixed. In Buffon's case, however, they may well have been entirely negative. Buffon had never fully mastered all the complexities of the apparently simple experimental method. He was enormously impressed by the arduous labors of men like Woodward and Hales, but he never actually attempted, except in brief spasms, a thoroughgoing imitation of their example. Other men could gather the facts; he was content to attempt to order them, to explain them. In consequence he had undertaken the series of experiments on generation only when he had secured the assistance of a man he had every reason to believe was one of the most eminent of the virtuosi of the Royal Society of London, a master of the exacting art of the experiment, possessing an instinctive grasp of the need for caution, for constant rechecking. Now, there can have been few among the fellows of the Royal Society in 1748 less suited to fill that role than John Turberville Needham; his reputation as a skilled experimenter was based largely on his exceptional manual dexterity. Few men were less naturally cautious, more ready for intellectual adventures.

At the conclusion of the experiments Buffon was unshakably convinced that his speculations on generation had been verified by experimentation. This conviction was evidently due, to a considerable degree, to the presence of Needham, the virtuoso from London, the expert microscopist, who had corroborated every detail of his observations. Buffon's total commitment to the theory of organic molecules was, therefore, in a very real sense, a direct consequence of the Needham-Buffon collaboration. And this uncritical commitment would, for Buffon, forever block the way to any further discoveries in this area.

CHAPTER 7

A Precursor of Darwin?

I *An Encumbered Traveler*

IN the beginning Buffon's thought was characterized, to a remarkable degree, by freedom from preconceptions of any
kind. However, after the publication of his first major theoretical
essays in the three introductory volumes of the *Histoire Naturelle*
in 1749, Buffon's resemblance to that classic figure of modern
existentialist fiction, the traveler without luggage, had largely
disappeared. Through the twelve volumes of the *Histoire Naturelle des Quadrupèdes* (1753–67), the nine volumes of the *Histoire Naturelle des Oiseaux* (1770–83), the seven volumes of
Suppléments (1774–89), and the five volumes of the *Histoire
Naturelle des Minéraux* (1783–88), Buffon was confronted with
an orthodoxy far more constraining than the ecclesiastical orthodoxy with which his *Théorie de la Terre* had briefly collided, for
it was a Buffonian orthodoxy. The general views enunciated in
the great volumes of 1749 shaped, to a considerable extent, everything that was to follow.

This luggage proved particularly burdensome in Buffon's efforts
to interpret the complex patterns of resemblance and variation he
found as he proceeded through the long descriptive sections of
the natural histories of the quadrupeds (i.e., land mammals) and
birds. He could not discover, in the process of writing these endless descriptions, a new and more viable general theory that
would account for similarities and differences among the many
species he studied with such painstaking care, because he had
begun with a theory that explained far too much far too easily:
the organic molecules and their *moules,* and the spontaneous
generations they made possible. Because of his unshakable belief
in the validity of the experiments he had performed with Needham in 1748, this prior commitment proved inescapable. A letter

Buffon wrote to Filippo Pirri on November 8, 1776, suggests something of the firmness of his convictions in this area:

> I confess to you that I am unable to take seriously M. Spallanzani's supposed discoveries, and I am astonished to find that you are willing to concede that he has demonstrated, beyond any possibility of doubt, that spermatic worms and infusorial worms are true animals, divided into species which are at once distinctly different from all others and easily recognizable. Nothing is less proved, or, to put it more accurately, nothing is more false than that assertion. M. Spallanzani has seen in the seminal fluids only what I myself saw long before him. However, it has pleased him to call *animals* moving bodies which in no way merit that name, and which are in truth only the preliminary *aggregations* of the living organic molecules.[1]

Some of the consequences of Buffon's total adherence to the theory of organic molecules are apparent in a famous passage of the second volume of *Suppléments,* published in 1775, in which he addressed himself, with his customary confidence, to the subject of life on other worlds:

> We must therefore conclude, from the general results of our experiments [with regard to the rate of cooling of heated globes] that . . . thirteen of the planetary bodies . . . are capable at the present time of supporting the existence of organized beings, and it is permissible to believe that all of these planetary bodies are, like the terrestrial globe, covered with plants, and even peopled with creatures endowed with sensation, which are quite similar to the animals of the earth. We shall demonstrate elsewhere, by bringing together a great number of detailed observations, that in all places where the temperature is the same, one finds, not only the same species of reptiles, which have not been transported from other regions, but also the same species of fish, the same species of quadrupeds, the same species of birds, none of which have emigrated to the regions in which they are found. . . . The same temperature nourishes, and calls into being, everywhere, the same species. . . . (H.N.S. II, p. 508)

Thus, by the simple expedient of hypothesizing a finely adjusted interrelationship between heat and the life force, which he had described thirty years before as one of the basic properties of matter—manifesting itself both in the frenetic movements of the organic molecules and in the shaping power of the *moules—*

Buffon was able to account for the geographical distribution of all living creatures, and even to make startling predictions concerning their extraterrestrial distribution.

The assumed interconnection of life and heat, both basic properties of matter, a connection involving adjustments in the functioning of the *moules* in response to temperature changes, also made possible an explanation of both the many variations in outer form among certain species of animals and the extraordinary similarity of their internal organs revealed by comparative anatomical studies. The most important features of the *moules,* those that determined the size and general nature of the creatures formed by the assembling of organic molecules, were directly determined, Buffon suggested, by the particular temperature of the habitat; certain other features of the *moules,* however, such as those relating to the circulatory and digestive systems, were little affected by temperature, and, consequently, these organs varied little from species to species.

Gigantic fossil bones were explained by the same mechanisms. In the *Epoques de la Nature* in 1778 Buffon attributed the original creation of the organic molecules to the action of intense heat on "ductile matters" at an early stage in the formation of the earth's land masses. At the time of their first appearance the organic molecules were rendered so active by their superheated environment that vast numbers of them were able to coalesce and to shape themselves spontaneously into awesome and gigantic creatures. These first, primitive creatures vanished suddenly, abruptly, as the temperature of the rapidly cooling globe fell to a point below which they could not function effectively, and new forms, *moules* adapted to slower molecules, arose to take their place, a process that was potentially without end:

If the greater part of the creatures about us were suddenly suppressed, one would see new species appear, because these organic molecules, which are indestructible and always active, would join together to form other organized bodies; but, as they are entirely absorbed by the *moules intérieurs* of presently existing creatures, new species cannot now be formed, at least in the major categories, such as the large animals. . . . (H.N.S. V, p. 184)

Buffon had come in time to regard Needham's infusions, in which he had "observed" the spontaneous generation of "worms" and "eels" in 1748, as microscopic models of the superheated world on which, thousands of years before, a great variety of large and complex creatures, many of which resembled each other rather closely, had suddenly come into existence. Once its initial premises had been accepted, there was little that such a theory could not explain.

II *Butler and the "Buffonians"*

It would seem, at first glance, that Buffon's explanations of the origin of the different species, extrapolated from his theory of generation, had more in common with the nightmarish visions of the beginnings of things offered by the pre-Socratic Greek philosopher and poet Empedocles of Sicily, or anybody's primitive creation myth, than it had with the system of natural selection rigorously formulated by Charles Darwin some seventy years after Buffon's death. But, to many commentators, Buffon's role in the development of the concept of species, and the kindred idea of evolution, has appeared to be far more subtle and extensive than the orthodox Buffonian theory might indicate. Long before the publication of Charles Darwin's *Origin of Species,* all through the eighteenth and the first half of the nineteenth century, men such as Benoît de Maillet, Erasmus Darwin, Lamarck, and Robert Chambers had brought versions of evolutionary theory before the general reading public. The basic concept of evolution—the idea that living forms are exposed at all times to powerful modifying forces and that, given an adequate expanse of time, a single original form might well have given rise to all of the existing varieties—was the subject of much speculation, some of it quite impressive. Consequently, when Charles Darwin's definitive work finally appeared in 1859, launching a great controversy throughout the civilized world, and evolution came at last to be accepted as respectable by the bulk of reputable professional scientists, Darwin's right to be considered the founder of the new doctrine was sometimes questioned. And, in the lists of Darwin's "predecessors" compiled by his opponents, Buffon's name often figured rather prominently.

The most determined defense of Buffon's "rights" in the matter was contained in a work published by Samuel Butler, the author of *Erewhon,* in 1879, entitled *Evolution, Old and New, or the Theories of Buffon, Dr. Erasmus Darwin, and Lamarck, as Com-*

pared with that of Charles Darwin. Butler's most strenuous objection was to the dominant role assigned to chance variation in the Darwinian theory. He preferred to regard evolution as the unfolding of a preordained design, and he advanced, as an alternative theory, an "opinion . . . suggested in the first instance and carried out to a very high degree of development by Buffon," namely, "that the design which has designed organisms, has resided within, and been embodied in, the organisms themselves." [2] This is a recognizable description of Buffon's theory of *moules,* and, in the early section of the work in which this passage appears, Butler's interpretation of Buffon is quite conservative, and unquestionably valid, but he soon moved his argument onto less solid ground, attributing to Buffon the views:

. . . that not only are many species mutable, but that all living forms, whether animal or vegetable, are descended from a single, or at any rate from not many, original low forms of life, and this as the direct consequence of the actions and requirements of the living forms themselves, and as the indirect consequence of changed conditions. A definite cause is thus supposed to underlie variations, and the resulting adaptations become purposive. . . .[3]

Now, Buffon had been obliged, in the descriptive articles on quadrupeds and birds that make up the greater part of the *Histoire Naturelle,* to point out, again and again, considerable variations within individual species, and he had suggested that the effects of climate, changes in nutrition, and domestication were to be regarded as the chief causative factors in these variations, or "degenerations." But he never abandoned the position that the species themselves were a fact of nature, indeed a physical property of matter, and that the first members of each of the known species had come into existence almost instantaneously, at the time when the cooling earth had reached the appropriate temperature, the temperature at which unused organic molecules could group themselves into organisms in accord with the *moules* of those particular species. Butler, however, did not find Buffon's stated position an obstacle to his own design of presenting the great French naturalist to the world as the true founder of modern evolutionary views:

I am inclined to think that a vein of irony pervades the whole, or much the greater part of Buffon's work, and that he intended to convey one meaning to one set of readers, and another to another; indeed, it is often impossible to believe that he is not writing between his lines for the discerning, what the undiscerning were not intended to see
. . . .
It is probably for the reasons above suggested [fear of the ecclesiastical authorities] that Buffon did not propound a connected scheme of evolution or descent with modification, but scattered his theory in fragments up and down his work in the prefatory remarks with which he introduces the more striking animals or classes of animals. He never wastes evolutionary matter on the preface to an uninteresting animal; and the more interesting the animal, the more evolution will there be commonly found.[4]

Butler's contention that in the *Histoire Naturelle* it is not the lines of print but the spaces between them that are to be consulted obviously legitimizes a certain latitude in the interpretations of the "discerning" reader. But, as he picked his way through Buffon's "prefatory remarks," Butler often had such surprisingly good luck that he was able at many points to dispense entirely with allusions to the prevailing Buffonian irony which he had been the first to discover, possibly because he was one of the few commentators ever to approach this section of Buffon's work in a literary rather than a scientific spirit. Butler's most striking find was perhaps the following fragment, culled from a passage in Buffon's article on the ass, of 1753:

. . . if we once admit that there are families of plants and animals, so that the ass may be of the family of the horse, and that the one may only differ from the other through degeneration from a common ancestor, we might be driven to admit that the ape is of the family of man, that he is but a degenerate man, and that he and man have had a common ancestor, even as the ass and horse have had. It would follow then that every family whether animal or vegetable, had sprung from a single stock, which after a succession of generations, had become higher in the case of some of its descendants and lower in that of others
. . . .
then there is no further limit to be set to the power of nature, and we should not be wrong in supposing that with sufficient time she could have evolved all other organized forms from one primordial type. (H.N. IV, p. 381)[5]

Often, however, Butler had to beat a hasty retreat to the spaces between the lines, as in his reaction to Buffon's assertion that man alone is endowed with reason:

I am ashamed of even arguing seriously against the supposition that this was Buffon's real opinion. The very sweepingness of the assertion, the baldness, and I might say brutality with which it is made, are convincing in their suggestiveness of one who is laughing very quietly in his sleeve.[6]

On the whole, Butler's approach was so completely innocent of all objectivity that it does not seem entirely unjust to dismiss his views as the vagaries of an intemperate and eccentric polemicist. A writer of the first rank is not easily dismissed, however, and, through the years, a number of distinguished commentators have supported, to some extent, Butler's assessment of Buffon's importance in the development of the concept of evolution. George Bernard Shaw, in the preface to *Back to Methuselah,* enthusiastically seconded Butler's most extreme views, and even Charles Darwin himself accorded Buffon a position of importance among his predecessors. More recently, Loren Eiseley, in his *Darwin's Century, Evolution and the Men Who Discovered It,* presented an appraisal of Buffon's role that bears an unmistakable resemblance to Butler's:

It is a great pity that his [Buffon's] ideas were scattered and diffused throughout the vast body of his *Natural History* with its accounts of individual animals. Not only did this concealment make his interpretation difficult, but it lessened the impact of his evolutionary ideas
. . . .
However, almost everything necessary to originate a theory of natural selection existed in Buffon. It needed only to be brought together and removed from the protective ecclesiastical coloration which the exigencies of his time demanded.[7]

III   *A Rebuttal of Butler*

In 1956, J. S. Wilkie of University College, London, undertook, in a lengthy monograph, a formal refutation of Butler's position.[8] Retracing Butler's progress through Buffon's "prefatory remarks" he reset the carefully selected citations of *Evolution, Old and New* within the framework of Buffon's acknowledged general views.

This process alone proved sufficient to undercut the greater part of Butler's arguments.

The "evolutionary" passage in the article on the ass, for example, was written at a time when Buffon was making his strongest stand against the taxonomy of Linnaeus, and in this context it appears to be intended as an illustration of the patently absurd consequences of any rigidly systematic attempt to group all species into families, a *reductio ad absurdum* rather than open advocacy. At that time, it is quite evident, if one does not regard Buffon primarily as a Voltairian ironist, that he felt that the mere suggestion that plants and animals could be descended from a single common ancestor was certain to provoke the derisive laughter of all reasonable men.

Wilkie also amassed evidence in support of the view that Buffon had found in his theory of generation alternative answers to the questions the evolutionists were struggling to resolve, an interpretation of Buffon's position previously adopted by Jean Rostand and Paul Ostoya.[9] Jacques Roger, in his critical edition of the *Epoques de la Nature* in 1962 and in his *Les Sciences de la vie dans la pensée française du XVIIIᵉ siècle* of 1963, buttressed this position with a wealth of new documentation, citing fresh and relevant passages not only in Buffon's "prefactory remarks" but in the individual descriptive articles as well.[10] In sum, modern scholarship has brought to bear on what Wilkie called "the rather suspect ingenuity of Samuel Butler" a crushing weight of adverse evidence. No amount of ingenuity, or appeals to irony, can offset the fact that Buffon at no point proposed a mechanism by which unlimited variability could be explained, and that he did formally propose, and incessantly allude to, a mechanism for the spontaneous generation of highly complex creatures.

IV *The Continued Evolution of a Theory*

The studies of both Wilkie and Roger have made it clear, however, that, although Buffon's theory of organic molecules did effectively block the path to thoroughgoing Darwinian views, his own thought in this area did undergo a considerable development in the course of his career, and this progress was generally in the direction of a very limited theory of evolution. Despite the great weight of the luggage that he carried, the natural agility of Buffon's thought continued to assert itself; in his persistent efforts to reconcile intractable facts with the theory he had so confidently adopted, he advanced steadily toward a better solution.

In the earlier volumes of the *Histoire Naturelle* Buffon had assumed that all of the known mammals could be grouped into two hundred species and the "varieties" of those species.[11] The species themselves sprang from the original *moules,* which, as we have seen, he regarded as innate and unvarying physical properties of matter itself, and the "varieties" were derived from the species by a process of "degeneration," the effect of climate, food, or domestication. As the "varieties" were in truth only slightly deformed exemplars of a single species they should all be capable of producing fertile offspring by interbreeding with other varieties of the same species. In order to verify these assumptions he undertook a series of experiments in animal hybridization, and in the process ran into the first of a long series of "theoretical" crises, crises that would oblige him again and again to make adjustments in his original premises.

Possibly because of errors in the conduct of the experiments, he found that some of his hybrids, involving the crossbreeding of totally different species, were not, like the common mule, invariably sterile; many were, it appeared, fully capable of producing fertile offspring of their own. He was thus forced to conclude that entirely new species could arise through interbreeding, and that there were indeed "families" of species.

The next major crisis arose when he attempted to expand his classificatory system to include the animals of the New World. Having found that many of these new species, although obviously related to species of the Old World, nevertheless differed from them in inexplicably subtle ways, he was forced to conclude that "degeneration" had effects far more profound and extensive than he had originally assumed. The adverse effects of climate might explain how a leopard could dwindle to an ocelot, but no such blunt, generalized force could explain the many, much more intricate differences he could not help but observe when he attempted to relate the tapir to the elephant or the llama to the camel. It is noteworthy that, in the next century, comparable differences, the myriad shapes assumed by the beaks of the finches of the Galápagos Archipelago, were eventually to convince Charles Darwin, after long hesitation, that climatic changes were not in fact among

the primary factors in the transformation process. Buffon, however, could always fall back on his original theory, and, rather
than seek a more adequate mechanism for "degeneration," he
chose to assume that tapirs and llamas were not degenerate elephants and camels but rather the products of a much later series
of spontaneous generations. He assumed that the landmasses of
the New World had been formed at a much more recent date
than those of the Old World, formed at a time when the unused
organic molecules had already lost much of their pristine vigor.
The somewhat jaded condition of the organic molecules explained
the rather distorted and inferior forms of the *moules* resulting
from this belated series of spontaneous generations.[12]

Buffon applied this explanation only to the ten "species" of
mammals which he felt were peculiar to the New World. In the
cases of the thirty "species" which he regarded as common to
both the Old and the New Worlds, assuming that they had entered the New World from the Old by way of land bridges prior
to the final division of the continents, he considered all changes in
form, however complex and extensive, as due exclusively to "degeneration."[13] The increased amplitude thus given to the "degeneration" concept, however, was sufficient to oblige him to regroup
his two hundred mammalian species into thirty-eight families.

The theory underwent even more drastic crises when Buffon
completed the sections of the *Histoire Naturelle* devoted to the
mammals and turned to the birds. Finding himself confronted
with, by his own count, some two thousand distinct species of
birds, he definitively, and unabashedly, turned to a classificatory
system based on three categories: genus, species, and "variety."
Jacques Roger has pointed out, however, that these progressive
modifications in Buffon's taxonomy were not accompanied by any
statements that might indicate a real change in his original view
of the species as a basic property of matter.[14] Nevertheless, the
changes made were both extensive and obvious, and the Marquis
de Condorcet, in his eulogy of Buffon in 1788, noted, with appropriate sarcasm, that the great opponent of Linnaeus had himself
become in the course of time *"un nomenclateur infatigable."*[15]

These changes in taxonomy, moreover, were cumulative and
in sum they constituted a major reorientation of Buffon's thought.
At the commencement of his career he had accepted Aristotle's
view of nature as an essentially static entity, in which the few

changes that did occur were both minor and reversible.[16] In time, however, he had come to recognize that nature is also subject to changes that are drastic in scope and absolutely irreversible, completely permanent. He had arrived at the concept of a world that is constantly in process of creation.[17] Jacques Roger has seen in this change in Buffon's general viewpoint, from static to dynamic, the major motivation behind his decision to return to his unfinished cosmogony in the 1770's and to convert it from a "theory" of the earth, an explanation of a closed system, into a "history" of the earth, a description of ongoing processes. And Pierre Teilhard de Chardin, who has in our own time attempted to add a metaphysical dimension to the concept of evolution, saw in this transformation of Buffon's thought, from closed to open, a first essential step in "the discovery of evolution," one of the most crucial of the "stages in man's awakening to the immensities of the cosmos, space and time":

After the walls of space, shaken by the Renaissance, it was the floor (and consequently the ceiling) of time which from Buffon onwards, became mobile. Since then, under the increasing pressure of facts, the process has continually accelerated.[18]

J. S. Wilkie, too, on a somewhat more mundane level, has also assigned to Buffon a role of the first importance in the development of the fundamental concepts that would eventually serve as the basis for a viable theory of evolution:

It is, I think, certainly true that Buffon was the first to attempt an empirical approach to the idea of organic evolution, subjecting it to the test of application to a wide range of data, much of which he himself had brought together for the first time.[19]

V *The Long Discovery*

On the basis of the facts alone, then, without recourse to Butlerian "suspect ingenuity," it has been made clear, by J. S. Wilkie, Jacques Roger, and others, that Buffon did make broad and important contributions to the early progress of modern biological thought, though these may touch upon Darwinian evolutionary theory itself only peripherally and in points of detail. Nevertheless, the discredit into which Butler's principal thesis has fallen should not lead us to discount his insights entirely. Wilkie himself, in the very process of exploding Butler's arguments, occasionally appeared to be following his example, approaching Buffon's text cautiously and with ready imagination:

[Buffon] is simply arguing one side of the case like a skilled barrister, pleased to show how well he can support either brief.

To conclude, it seems probable that Buffon held many theoretical positions which he was too intelligent to believe he had proved. It was, therefore, easy for him to present strongly and without any dishonesty the difficulties against his position. . . .[20]

We must not be too quick to identify what Buffon pronounced publicly, however much internal consistency we may find in it, with what he himself firmly believed. His thought was often far more subtle, and shifting, than the geometrical precision of his systems might indicate.

Buffon's influence on his contemporaries stemmed from his judicious examination and ordering of the "givens" of the many problems he attacked to at least as great an extent as it did from the solutions he eventually proposed. His contribution, in fact, was often limited to this clarification of the question, a bringing into focus of the all-important *Fragestellung*. Thus, his influence is often perceptible in the work of men whose final views were at a far remove from his own. The "evolutionary" passage from the article on the ass, for example, may well have exerted considerable influence on such contemporary English evolutionists as Erasmus Darwin, whom Butler inaccurately styled "a pupil of Buffon," inasmuch as that particular section of the *Histoire Naturelle* was published, out of context, in English translation as early as 1762, as *The Natural History of the Horse*. Various points of resemblance to Buffon in thought and procedure in the work of Erasmus Darwin, which were signaled by Butler, add support to this supposition. Furthermore, both Wilkie and Jacques Roger have suggested that Buffon may have exerted a similar influence on Lamarck, the best known of the early evolutionists. Lamarck actually was, briefly, Buffon's protégé, employed as a tutor for the young Count de Buffon.

Jacques Roger has epitomized Buffon's career in the phrase "that long discovery of nature which was the writing of the *Histoire Naturelle*," [21] and in his commentaries on the *Histoire Na-*

turelle he has made clear the surprising degree to which this protracted process of discovery was reflected in Buffon's writings. Butler's insistence upon the need to consult the spaces between the lines in reading Buffon retains a measure of validity for modern interpreters. Buffon's great concern for order made it impossible for him to abandon capriciously positions he considered basically sound, to plunge once more into the maelstrom of unrestricted speculation at a late point in his career, but the Buffonian orthodoxy he himself had created could only discipline, not shackle, the continued progress of his thought. If we can accept this point of view, take seriously the many "hints" to his successors in which Buffon's writings seem to abound, we will gain a more accurate impression of the range of his influence, and more easily understand his enormous contemporary reputation. He was a man of systems, ultimately faithful to them, but he was also a man fond of launching loose ideas into the public domain, of suggesting interesting possibilities to others. He did, as has often been said, ask all the right questions. Many of the answers, to be sure, still remain to be found.

CHAPTER 8

The Nature of Man

I *A Lockean Adam in Action*

IN the series of essays that made up the "Natural History of Man" in the second and third volumes of the *Histoire Naturelle*, with important extensions in the fourth general volume and in the fourth volume of supplements, Buffon often gave relatively free rein to his artistic impulses. This is particularly evident in what might be called his "Adam in Eden" passage, in the essay *"Des Sens en général"* (H.N. III, pp. 363–70).

The "first man" Buffon conjures up, and permits to speak at great length, in this his one surviving effort at literary characterization, is, however, disconcertingly unprimitive. Buffon's Adam sounds very much like a man formally addressing the Académie Royale des Sciences, sounds in fact very much like a member of that august and erudite assembly, detailing to his duly impressed *confrères* his own most astonishing discoveries: the existence of life, and the material world, and personal identity. Buffon, nevertheless, felt it necessary to alert his readers to an unexampled emotionalism of tone in this fragment:

I shall attempt to visualize, then, through the imagination, a man in the state in which the very first man must have found himself at the moment of the Creation, that is to say, a fully mature man, whose body and organs would be perfectly formed, but who would awaken, for the first time, entirely new, new to every part of himself and every aspect of his being, and new to everything that surrounds him. What would be his first movements, his first sensations, his first judgments? If such a man wished to retrace for us the history of his first thoughts, what would he tell us? What would be the nature of his story? I have no choice but to allow him to speak for himself, to render his account as he felt it. This philosophical fiction, which will be short, will not prove a pointless digression:

"I remember that instant full of joy and confusion, in which I be-

125

came aware for the first time of my singular existence; I did not know
what I was, where I was, or where I had come from. I opened my
eyes; what overwhelming superabundance of sensation! the light, the
great arch of the sky, the green things of the earth, the crystal water,
everything I saw absorbed me, excited me, gave me an inexpressible
feeling of pleasure; I believed at first that all these things were inside
me, were part of me.

"I gained confidence in this almost-born thought when I turned my
eyes toward the blazing star of light; its brilliance stabbed at me; in-
voluntarily, I shut my eyes, and I felt a small pain, a discomfort. In
that moment of darkness, of obscurity, I believed that I had lost almost all of my being.

"Suffering, astonished, I turned my thoughts to this great change,
when, suddenly, I heard noises; the singing of birds, the murmuring
of the winds, forming a concert of soft sounds that stirred me to the
bottom of my soul; for a long time I listened, and soon convinced myself that this harmony and I were one and the same.

"Totally attentive, completely absorbed in this new species of existence, I had completely forgotten the light, that other part of my being that I had known first, when I opened my eyes again. What joy to
find myself once more in possession of so much brilliance, of so many
shining objects! my pleasure surpassed everything I had felt the first
time, and suspended for a moment the charming effect of the sounds.

"I looked intently upon a thousand divers objects, and I soon perceived that I had the power both to lose sight of these objects and to
find them again, power to destroy and recreate at will this beautiful
part of myself. . . ."

Buffon's literal minded and rigidly logical Adam next discovers
the existence of scents, in the heavily perfumed breezes, and
suddenly experiences "a feeling of love for myself." He rises, in
his excitement, and takes his first step, and is immediately over-
come with panic:

". . . the movement I had made had displaced, confused, all objects; I
imagined that everything, literally everything, had been thrown into
disorder.

I lifted my hand to my head; I touched my forehead and my eyes;
I moved my hand over my entire body; my hand appeared to me then
as the principal organ of my existence . . . I could feel my ideas
taking on new depth and reality.

Every part of my body that I touched seemed to answer my hand,
returning feeling for feeling, and each lingering touch generated in my
soul a twofold idea."

"It was not long before I perceived that this faculty of touch was distributed throughout all the parts of my body; I soon recognized the limits, the boundaries, of my existence, which had at first seemed to me so vast in extent."

It is not long, however, before complexity, momentarily vanquished, reasserts its rights over the first man:

". . . I placed my hand very close to my eyes, and my hand seemed to me then to be larger than all the rest of my body, and it caused an infinite number of objects to vanish from my sight.

I began to suspect that something illusory was involved in these sensations that came to me through my eyes; I had seen distinctly that my hand was only a very small part of my body, and I could not understand how its size could have been augmented to so excessive a degree; I resolved therefore to place confidence only in my sense of touch, which had not yet deceived me, and to be on my guard against all other forms of being and feeling.

"This precaution proved useful: I had begun to move again, and I walked with my head held high, my face lifted toward the sky; I bumped, lightly, into a palm tree; completely terrified, I placed my hand on this foreign body; I judged it to be such because it did not return feeling for feeling; I turned from it with a kind of horror, and I knew for the first time that something existed apart from me."

Touch, however, does not prove a final answer to all of Adam's problems. He discovers that he can touch neither the sun nor the horizon, entirely unexpected and perplexing setbacks:

"Profoundly preoccupied with myself, with what I was, with what I might be, I found the difficulties I had just experienced humiliating; the more I reflected, the more doubts presented themselves; exhausted by uncertainties, fatigued with the very movments of my soul, I bent my knees, and found myself in a position of rest. This state of tranquility brought new strength to my senses; I was seated in the shadow of a beautiful tree, fruits of a vermilion color. . . ."

Fascinated by their odor, he plunges one of the fruits into his mouth, tastes it, and once again crosses a new frontier of sensation:

"Until then I had known only pleasures; taste gave me the sensation of voluptuousness, of ecstasy. The intimate quality of the enjoyment gen-

erated in my mind the idea of possession; I believed the substance of
this fruit had become my own substance, and that I was master of the
power to transform existing beings."

Sleep follows this supreme mental effort, sleep that is itself followed by Adam's familiar fright when he awakens—and by
something more, the ultimate discovery:

". . . while I explored with my eyes the limits and edges of my body
to assure myself that the extent of my existence had not been dimin-
ished, to my intense surprise I discovered at my side a form much like
my own! I took it for another me; far from having lost anything during
the period in which I had temporarily ceased to be, I had, I believed,
actually been doubled.

I explored this new being with my hand: what astonishment! it was
not I; rather, it was more than I, better than I: I believed that my existence was about to shift in space, to pass entirely into this second
half of myself.

I could feel life stirring in the body beneath my hand; I saw it respond, with thought, to the thought in my eyes; as I looked into its
eyes I felt new sources of life flowing in my veins: I determined that I
would willingly surrender my entire being to this creature; this act of
will completed my existence, and I felt a new kind of sensation being
born.

In that instant, the bright torch of the star of day was extinguished;
but I scarcely perceived that I was losing my sense of sight. I now felt
my existence too strongly to experience any new fears that I might
cease to be."

The point of this long and fanciful digression, which Buffon
hoped would not prove pointless, was a demonstration of the
theory of the generation of ideas from primal sensations that John
Locke had set forth in the *Essay Concerning Human Understanding* (1690). Locke had held that all human concepts and ideas, no
matter how complex or abstract, had their origin in a process of
interaction between simple sense impressions. Buffon attempted,
in his freely imaginative sketch of Adam's first groping explorations of his own body and the world around him, to suggest
definite links between certain specific types of ideas and particular sensory impulses. Like most contemporary French Lockeans,
he felt ideas could take on solidity and finality only if linked to
the sense of touch. He tied voluptuousness to taste and self-love

to smell. Most strikingly, though, he traced Adam's ultimate assurance of the reality of his own identity to the first awakening of his sexuality, following the discovery of Eve at his side, sexuality conceived in broadly idealistic terms as a supreme impulse toward giving, a desire for the total surrender of self.

II Condillac's Statue, and Critique

The Abbé Etienne Bonnot de Condillac, one of the most voluminous writers of the age, appropriated and expanded Buffon's first-man device in his *Traité des Sensations* (1754). Condillac imagined a statue whose outer layers only were stone and whose interior contained all the living organs of a human body. He proceeded to endow his statue with one sense at a time, beginning with the sense of smell, pausing each time he added a particular sense to trace the formation of new sets of ideas, deriving them either directly from the new sense or from interactions between all the senses then operative. Whatever shadings Buffon's sketch may have had of the arbitrary or the overly systematic, these pale before the unflinching rigor of the learned abbé. Condillac's man-statue had its share of admirers among the general literary public, but many of the wits of the salons professed to find it hugely amusing, and even suggested that the idea had been stolen from Buffon, who had at least handled it with grace. "It was said at the time," wrote Baron Grimm, "that the Abbé de Condillac had drowned M. de Buffon's statue in a vat of cold water." [1]

Condillac reacted, in his *Traité des Animaux* (1755), with a savage critique of Buffon's original sketch. Locke and Buffon alike, he affirmed, had left out crucial steps in the process by which "the system of our insights" is formed from "combinations of a small number of sensations." Locke "did not know that we must learn to touch, learn to see, learn to hear, etc.," and Buffon "assumes [a sense of the] present, without any preparation, in the man he imagines, habits and skills that he would have had first to acquire, to learn." Moreover, Condillac found some of the connections Buffon did make a bit bizarre: "Are we really to believe that the ability to perceive odors is the sole basis of self-love?" But Condillac seemed incensed above all by the immense popularity enjoyed by Buffon's work, a popularity that had as yet eluded his own books: "In effect, if your principles are vague, and involve contradictions, and you reason little, or your reasoning is inconsistent, your words will be heeded by the entire world." [2]

Buffon the much admired writer and *philosophe* continued to be Condillac's preferred target as he broadened his attack to include all that Buffon had written of sensation and understanding. The typical *philosophe*, Condillac averred, is wont to "mistake a metaphor for an exact notion," and he ridiculed in particular Buffon's use of the then popular comparison of the action of the nerves to the regular vibrating of a taut cord.[3] At times, his eagerness to denigrate Buffon led him to distort his own position. He insisted that Buffon had established too rigid a differentiation between the mental processes of man and the mental processes of animals. If, in fact, animals have sensation, and, in theory, sensation generates ideas, then, in theory, animals must have ideas: "The beaver first imagines the dwelling it is to build; the bird, the nest it wants to construct. These animals would not make these things if the imagination did not give them the models for them." [4] Condillac did not hesitate even to impute reflection, the ability to make reasoned comparisons, to animals, but in the latter parts of this same *Traité des Animaux* he returned gradually to a position very close to Buffon's: animals act from habit, only from habit; the habits have their origin in reflection, but the power of reflection ceases to function once the habits are firmly established; man alone retains the power of reflection throughout his life.[5]

In sum, Condillac's critique, though by far the most authoritative ever leveled at Buffon, suffers throughout from what was only too evidently a passionately felt—and finally self-defeating—aversion to everything Buffonian. Buffon's positions had elements of solidity that a more judicious critic would have been careful to acknowledge. Buffon had, for example, explored in considerable depth both the entire question of optical illusions and the manner in which we learn to use our sense of sight, learn to adapt to its built-in inaccuracies. The essay *"Du Sens de la Vue,"* which had preceded the Adam passage in the third volume of the *Histoire Naturelle,* was one of the most complete contemporary treatments of human vision and its aberrations. Buffon had examined "a great number" of people with eye defects, he had performed experiments, and he had collected, somewhat at random, a mass of very curious observations: "it is because we are not in the habit of judging distances in this direction that, when we find ourselves at the top of a high tower, the men and animals we see below seem to be much smaller than they would seem to be if they were an equal distance away horizontally, which is to say, in the direction in which we are accustomed to judge distances . . ."; "the lanterns along the road from Paris to Versailles, for example, often seem, when viewed from afar, say an eighth of a league, to be all on the right side, instead of on the left side, where they really are. . . ." In *"Du Sens de la Vue"* Buffon had also described, in full detail, the experiences of a man, blind since birth, whose sight had been restored by a cataract operation, as reported by the English surgeon Cheselden, and the experiences of Buffon's Adam closely duplicated many of those of Cheselden's patient. Buffon was thus, at many points, presenting not vague and self-contradictory theory, but hard facts, the results of meticulous observation.

Similarly, within the general context of contemporary physical science, Buffon's tendency to describe nerve functions in terms of vibrations was more than a *littérateur's* abuse of a metaphor. If one assumes that light is a form of matter, made up of a stream of very tiny particles of matter, then Buffon's contention that "seeing is a kind of touching" is entirely valid; the eye is responding to a bombardment of matter. And, in the absence of even a minimally sophisticated knowledge of chemistry and physiology, vibration phenomena did provide the most logical "models" for discussing nerve action. The writings of many psychologists of today, whose terminology with regard to mental operations often reflects the use of the computer as "model," may seem equally simplistic, or "wrong," to future generations.

III   *Homo Duplex?*

Buffon's position on the uniqueness of man, as enunciated in the short introductory essay *"De la Nature de l'Homme"* in the second volume of the *Histoire Naturelle,* was much closer to conventional theological thinking than that of his dogged clerical adversary, the Abbé de Condillac:

We have said that nature always advances and acts in all things by imperceptible degrees and nuances: this truth, which elsewhere admits of no exceptions, proves totally false here. There is an infinite distance between the mental faculties of man and those of the most perfect ani-

mal, evident proof that man is of a different nature, that he alone constitutes a class apart, from which one must descend, through an un-
imaginably vast expanse of space, to reach the animals.

In much of this crucial introductory essay to his writings on
man, Buffon frankly adopted both the terminology and the view-
points of the theologians, answering in the affirmative his own
rhetorical question: "Should some consideration of the soul have
a place in a work of natural history?" He offered both definitions
of the soul, more Cartesian than original, and proofs of its existence: "Our soul has only one form, which is very simple, very
general, and very constant; that form is thought"; "The existence
of our soul is evident to us, most demonstrable, or, rather, we are
one single entity, that existence and us; to be and to think are for
us the same thing; this is an intimate truth, more than intuitive;
it is independent of our senses, of our imagination, of our memory,
and of all our other faculties that relate and compare."

Many of the arguments Buffon presents here, in support of belief in the soul, were quite standard, and some seem calculatedly
naïve or even disingenuous. He laboriously demonstrates, for
example, that the range and mobility of thought, the vast sweeps
it makes in space and in time, are not the familiar qualities of
matter in motion, taken in the narrowest Cartesian sense. He
argues that the loss of specific senses, by blindness, deafness, or
leprosy, does not noticeably impair a man's ability to think. But
he offers, too, arguments of some weight and subtlety, new arguments, particularly with regard to the differences between men
and animals, beings with and without soul. He cites anatomical
studies of apes that indicated, seemingly, that some of these animals possess a vocal apparatus as sophisticated as man's: "Apes
would speak, then, if they could think . . . but no one has ever
seen them in conversation together . . . therefore they do not
have even a kind of ordering of thought, of linking of ideas, that
is peculiar to themselves, much less one similar to ours." Memory,
reflection, the comparison of ideas, the hallmarks of human
thought, Buffon repeatedly insists, are at the very root of the
difference:

Because animals cannot join together any ideas, they can neither think
nor speak; and it is for the same reason that they neither invent nor

perfect anything. If they were endowed with the power to reflect, even in the smallest degree, they would be capable of some sort of progress; their productivity would increase; the beavers of today would build with greater art and solidity than the first beavers; the bee would constantly perfect the cell it inhabits. . . . But no, all do their work according to the same model; the order in their actions is determined, fixed in set patterns, for the entire species, and it does not belong to the individual; if one wished to attribute a soul to animals, one would be obliged to provide only one soul for each species, a single soul in which every individual belonging to the species would have an equal share.

The inventiveness of man, the fact that "servile imitation is more burdensome to us than the creation of new designs," is Buffon's major argument here for the existence of individual human souls.

Somewhat disconcertingly, however, Buffon abruptly ended this essay, and his arguments, on a decidedly weak note: "Having considered the interior of man, and having demonstrated the spirituality of his soul, we can now proceed to examine the exterior of man, and trace the natural history of his body." This seems to relegate the introductory essay to the status of a precautionary counterweight, intended merely to redress the balance against the purely "scientific," and materialistic, consideration of man that was to follow. But, if this were entirely true, Condillac should have found very little to object to in Buffon's presentation of Lockean theory, and he found much. What took place within Buffon's Adam was quite apparently less the gradual creation of ideas through the interaction of sensations than the activation of a mechanism already present. Buffon did leave out step after step; he did assume the presence of concepts that Adam had had no opportunity to learn. The mind of Buffon's Adam was not a Lockean *tabula rasa*, a totally blank slate. And Buffon's procedures in the Adam essay correlate most significantly with important statements in the introductory "soul" essay, particularly his invocation there of a unique inner "sense" possessed by man:

Too exclusively occupied with the multiplication of our sense impressions, the augmentation of the outward extension of our being, we rarely use the internal sense that reduces us to our true dimensions. . . . But how are we to give this sense its full activity and range? How are we to free our soul, within which it resides, from all the illusions of our intellect? We have lost the habit of using it; it has remained without exercise amid the tumult of our corporal sensations, withered by the heat of our passions; the heart, the intellect, the senses, all have worked against it.

The fundamental human nature of Buffon's Adam was determined, to a considerable extent, before he began his explorations, determined by the *moule* of man, a *moule* that includes the ability to think creatively and critically, to make comparisons and judgments, and, almost, to be aware of personal identity, through the operations of an internal sense that resides "in the soul."

Buffon's discussion of the soul is the most convincing of his occasional, apologetic theological passages, possibly because much that had traditionally been said of the human soul could be applied, with only minor adjustments, to Buffon's own mysterious *moules.* An imperfect Lockean and a grudging Cartesian, Buffon had seemingly arrived, by the route of his own theories, at an affirmation of the dual nature of man, a product both of eternal *moule* and of contingent environmental pressures, that was roughly compatible with the soul-body dualism of the theologians.

In 1753, in the essays *"De la Nature des Animaux"* and *"Homo Duplex"* in the fourth volume of the *Histoire Naturelle,* Buffon returned once more to the subject of the distinctiveness of man, apparently determined to counter even the subtlest arguments that could be advanced against his views. These essays have the exhaustive illustrative examples, the grim repetitiveness, the frequent recapitulations, of a tireless lawyer's summation to the jury. They leave little doubt as to the sincerity of Buffon's own conviction.

In *"De la Nature des Animaux"* Buffon first divides the entity called animal life into successive layers, forcing his reader to admit that creatures like the oyster, although possessing the bottommost layer of aliveness, must lack additional layers that are available to the higher animals, a preliminary admission that, hopefully, will inevitably lead the reader to the final admission that there may well be topmost layers that are available to man alone. He then attempts to demonstrate that the behavior of even a well trained and affectionate dog can be adequately explained in terms of mechanistic "appetites." The dog that is given a command by his master that seems to cause it to resist its own instincts is simply "simultaneously pushed by two contrary impulses, which mutually destroy one another, and he remains in equilibrium between these two equal powers":

> One can explain in the same manner, and with the same principles, all the actions of animals, however complicated they may appear, without any need to accord to them either thought or reflection. . . . But then, people will say to us, do animals have no knowledge? Are you denying them even the knowledge, the feeling, of their own existence? Since you claim to explain all their actions mechanically, are you not reducing them to simple machines?
>
> If I have explained myself well, it should already be quite clear that, far from denying everything to animals, I accord everything to them, with the single exceptions of thought and reflection; they have feeling, sentiment, even to a higher degree than we have; they have also the awareness of their present existence, but not of their past existence; they have sensations, but not the ability to compare them, the power to draw ideas from them. . . .

He establishes here a basic distinction between human memory, which involves a capacity to visualize the past in a controlled and accurate manner, and animal *réminiscence,* which is simply a matter of patterns of vibration permanently impressed on the nervous system.

In *"Homo Duplex,"* the conclusive piece in the long argument, Buffon singles out types of human behavior that are without parallel among animals, behavior explainable only by the hypothesis of man's divided nature, in part animal and in part something quite different. Man alone is torn by internal "moral" conflict, the consequence of his ability to visualize opposing goals in their full complexity:

> I am referring to those periods of *ennui,* indolence, and disgust, in which we can decide nothing, in which we want what we do not do, and do what we do not want; to that state or that malady to which the name *vapors* has been given . . . in this state our ego appears to us to be divided into two persons, one, which represents the faculties of reason, condemns what the other does, but is not strong enough to vanquish. . . .

More important still, only man has created societies held together by abstract concepts of morality and duty, and enlightened self-

interest, cohesive forces that have nothing at all in common with
the blind, overmastering instincts of social insects or beavers:

> Among men, social organization depends less on physical convenience
> than on moral relations. . . . Man has reflected on the ideas of good
> and evil, has engraved them in his heart . . . he has sought security
> and peace in society . . . this coming together of men is man's finest
> work; it is the best use he has made of his reason. In effect, he is safe,
> he is strong, he is great, he governs the universe, only because he has
> been able to govern himself, to tame himself, to submit voluntarily and
> to impose laws upon himself; man, in a word, is man only because he
> has known how to join together with other men.

It is, then, in man's inner torment, his moral awareness, and in
the boundless complexity and diversity of the works of his intellect—qualities resulting from the peculiar plasticity of the human
moule—that Buffon finds, in the essay "*Homo Duplex*," the most
convincing evidence for that essay's opening maxim: "The inner
man is double, composed of two principles different in their
nature and contrary in their action."

IV *First Look at Anthropos*

One modern anthropologist, Walter Scheidt, has remarked of
Buffon: "he can frankly be called the 'first anthropologist,'" [6] and
Jean Piveteau, a scholar not noted for rash judgments, has written:
"One may see in Buffon one of the founders of anthropology, that
is to say, of the study of man as a species and not as an individual." [7] Buffon's efforts in "anthropology," however, his observations and comments on man as a species, a biological phenomenon,
a simple object to be viewed without theological or sentimental
preconceptions, are, throughout, among the least formalized, the
least rigorous, the least systematic, of all his writings. His general
approach usually seems freewheeling, loosely impressionistic.
These essays are more reminiscent of Montaigne than of Bossuet,
to whom Buffon is more customarily compared. At times they
bring to mind, rather than comparisons with the works of any of
the great lights of modern anthropology, a well-known malicious
personal comment on Buffon by Hérault de Séchelles:

> This great man has something of the village gossip in him; for at least
> one hour each day . . . he has his hairdresser and his house servants
> tell him everything that is going on in Montbard, and in his château. [8]

A conspicuous place in the advanced front ranks of a new discipline is not always an unmixed blessing. To Buffon the pioneer anthropologist it meant primarily entanglement in an immense welter of undigested fact. The data, minutely detailed accounts set down by generations of indefatigable travelers, voyagers, explorers, and sedentary prepsychologists, extending back at least to the early Renaissance, and not, of course, excluding Herodotus, Aristotle, or Pliny were so enormous, so heterogenous, and, often, so fantastic, that no final vision of order could successfully be imposed on them. And Buffon came to terms with the situation, in his own fashion, accepting multiplicity but at the same time clinging stubbornly to whatever rudiments of order he could find. Nevertheless, the sheer proliferation of detail throughout these essays, much of it frankly extraneous, the triumph everywhere of the tiny isolated fact, does at times create, irresistibly, an impression of the village gossip avidly assembling a dossier on Man.

The most consistent strategy employed by Buffon in his quest for form in the midst of chaos was the invocation of Natural Law. According to this quasi-mystic Enlightenment notion, there is always, in every situation in which man may conceivably find himself, a natural, or "right," course of action, one action out of the many that is dictated directly by Nature's Law. In all existing societies, however, even the most civilized, customs have grown up, and become entrenched, which are contrary to Natural Law, and have distorted human nature. Most particularly in his discussion of human sexual functions and the customs that regulate them, Buffon attempted to reveal such perversions of nature, both in distant lands and in his own France, by juxtaposing descriptions of suspect behavior with accounts of the evidently more rational practices of happier and more harmonious peoples. Needless to say, the piquancy of these subjects added to the interest of the *Histoire Naturelle*. Though his thought may seem to carom about like an unaimed billiard ball even in some of these passages, a central core of argumentation is never obscured:

In Madagascar, and in some other countries, the girls who are the most libertine and the most debauched are the first to be married. We could give several other examples of this extraordinary taste, which can only come from the crudity, or the depravity, of customs.

The natural state of man after puberty is marriage; a man should not have more than one wife, just as a woman should have no more than a single husband; this is nature's law, since the number of females is roughly equal to the number of males: it can therefore only be by departing from natural law, and by the most unjust of tyrannies, that men have established laws that differ from this. Reason, humanity, and justice cry out against the odious harem, where one sacrifices to the brutal or disdainful passion of a single man the liberty and the love of many women, each one fully capable of bringing complete happiness to another man. Are these tyrants of the human species happier? surrounded by eunuchs, and by women as useless to them as they are to other men, they are adequately punished: they see only the misery that they have created.

Marriage, as it is established among us and among the other rational and religious peoples is therefore the condition best suited to man, the condition in which he can best make use of the new faculties he has acquired at puberty, which would become a burden to him, and sometimes even a danger, if he should persist in maintaining celibacy. The too prolonged retention of the seminal fluid in its reservoirs can cause diseases, in both sexes, or at least irritations so violent that reason and religion are scarcely sufficient to resist these impetuous passions; they would reduce man to the level of the beasts, who are savage and ungovernable when they experience these impressions.

The most extreme effect of this irritation in women is nymphomania; this is a kind of madness that troubles the intellect and destroys all modesty and restraint; the most lascivious speech, the most indecent actions, accompany this tragic illness, and reveal its origin. I have seen, and I have seen it as a phenomenon of nature, a girl of twelve years, very dark, with a healthy and ruddy complexion, small in stature but already mature, with the breasts and full body of a woman, perform the most obscene actions at the mere sight of a man; nothing could restrain her, not the presence of her mother, not remonstrances, not punishment; she did not, however, lose her reason; and her seizures, which were horribly severe, ceased the moment she found herself alone with women. Aristotle claims that it is at this age that the irritation is greatest, and that it is necessary to guard young girls the most carefully. That may be true for the climate in which he lived, but it seems that in colder climates the temperament of women becomes ardent only much later.

When nymphomania has reached a certain point of severity, marriage does not calm it: there are examples of women who have died from it. Happily, nature alone is seldom the unique cause of these dangerous passions, even when the individual temperament is much disposed to them; to reach this extremity the concurrence of several causes is required, the principal being an imagination inflamed by licentious conversations and erotic and indecent images. The opposite temperament is infinitely more common among women; by far the greater number are naturally cold, or at least indifferent to the physical aspects of that passion. There are also men to whom chastity costs nothing; I have known men, who enjoyed good health, and who had reached twenty-five or thirty years without ever having experienced needs, imposed by nature, that were so pressing that they were obliged to satisfy them in any way.

Moreover, excess is more greatly to be feared than continence. The number of men who have been immoderate is great enough to furnish many examples: some have lost their memories, others have been deprived of sight, still others have become bald, some have perished from exhaustion. . . . (H.N. II, *"De l'Homme; De la Puberté"*)

Cautious, as ever, Buffon often seems to take two steps back for every step forward whenever what, echoing general Enlightenment opinion, he chose to regard as Natural Law infringed too closely upon established custom, particularly in sensitive areas like clerical celibacy. In the fourth volume of supplements, for example, he printed a very long autobiographical memoir sent to him in 1774 by a young man who had been driven into uncontrollable frenzies by the pressure of his vows of celibacy, to the point that he had torn a bedpost from his bed and hurled it at the door with such force that the door was dashed from its hinges, so that his guardians had had to chain him to his bed. But Buffon, after permitting this victim of continence to catalogue his miseries in excruciating detail, piously noted: "There are perhaps a thousand examples of people lost through excess for each person rendered ill by continence"; he did not, however, offer to present any of these in similar detail.

Buffon's most striking achievements in signaling violations of nature's laws in *ancien régime* France came in the essay *"De l'Enfance."* French babies, at least those of the upper classes, the reading classes, were usually tightly bound in swaddling clothes and given to nurse to peasant women. The travel books revealed more enlightened, more natural, customs almost everywhere else: "All the peoples who are content to cover or clothe their infants without binding them, do they not do better than we? The Siamese, the Japanese, the Hindus, the Negroes, the savages of Canada, those of Virginia, and of Brazil, and most of the peoples of the American tropics, allow their infants to lie entirely naked, on beds of suspended cotton. . . ." The frightening child mortality rates established by Buffon's statistics—one half of all the children born in France died before reaching the age of seven—made the nursing of infants a particularly crucial matter: "If mothers nursed their own children, there is evidence that they would be stronger and more vigorous: the milk of its mother should suit the child better than the milk of another woman, for the foetus is nourished in the womb by a fluid very similar to milk; the child is thus already accustomed, so to speak, to the milk of its mother, while the milk of another nurse would be a new nourishment, which is sometimes so different that he cannot easily become accustomed to it; one sees infants who cannot accommodate themselves to the milk of certain women become emaciated, languishing, and ill." Simple patriotism, moreover, recommended these efforts, since the numbers of its people "are, as one knows, the true riches of a nation."

Jean-Jacques Rousseau, who was among other things the eighteenth century's greatest launcher of new manners and fashions of thought, was particularly struck by these details, and, within a few years, he would convert much of the French aristocracy to these "Rousseauist" doctrines. Even the radically permissive educational doctrines advocated by Rousseau in *Emile* (1762) were to some extent anticipated by Buffon: "There are so many examples of the small success of efforts to educate children prematurely . . . that one might be led to believe that the best of all educations is the one that is the most ordinary, the one in which nature is not forced, the one that is the least severe, the one that is best proportioned, not to the strengths, but to the weaknesses of the child." (H.N. II, *"De l'Homme; De l'Enfance"*)

Buffon's views on racial differences are also singularly enlightened. Persuaded that the ability to interbreed established the unity of the human species beyond all question, and that the observable differences among men were merely the direct effects of differences in climate, food, and manner of life, he regarded the conventional lines of demarcation among human types as essentially arbitrary: "Finally, in examining in particular the different peoples who compose each of these black races, we shall find among them as many varieties as in the white races; we shall find all the nuances from brown to black, just as we found in the white races all the nuances from brown to white." (H.N. III, *"Variétés dans l'Espèce Humaine"*) He attributed skin color almost entirely to the effects of the sun, the cumulative inheritance of acquired traits.

In some cases, though, this process of change within the species, which he always called "degeneration," seems to be quite literally degeneration, in the most pejorative sense. Buffon had formed, for example, from the accounts of travelers, a particularly dim view of Lapps and Tartars: "Not only do these peoples resemble one another in their ugliness and small stature, the color of their hair and eyes, but they have all pretty much the same inclinations and manners: they are all equally brutish, superstitious, and stupid." (H.N. III, *"Variétés dans l'Espèce Humaine"*)

On the whole, however, Buffon's attitude toward his sources was both suspicious and critical. In 1777, at the beginning of the *Additions* to the essay *"Variétés dans l'Espèce Humaine,"* he formally stated his most basic reservations:

> In all my writings on natural history there is perhaps no other article as susceptible to additions, and even to corrections, as that on the varieties in the human species . . . it is obvious that I was obliged to seek most of the facts in the accounts of the most reputable travelers. Unfortunately, these accounts, though faithful in certain respects, are much less so in others; men who take the trouble to go and see things that are far away believe that the hardships they have borne entitle them to render their accounts more marvelous; what point is there in leaving one's country if one has nothing remarkable to show or to tell on one's return? Thus come the exaggerations, the fables and bizarre tales, with which travelers have soiled their writings, in the belief that they were ornamenting them. But an attentive wit, a knowledgeable philosopher, easily recognizes apocrypha that shock verisimilitude, or the order of nature. . . . (H.N.S. IV)

At times, Buffon's reliance on his own sense of the way things must be, his own intuitive grasp of Natural Law, stood him in good stead. Though in 1749 he quoted George Psalmanazar, the century's most notorious fraud and charlatan, on the peoples of the Far East, he drew no errors from these fabricated accounts, but instead a conviction that certain other travelers who had spoken of a race of people with tails in Formosa were not to be trusted. But this basic distrust served him badly in later years,

when there were available to him the accounts of a far more
reliable generation of travelers, men like Bougainville and Cap-
tain Cook, leaders of full-scale scientific expeditions sponsored by
the major academies. Long interviews about Abyssinia with the
great Scottish explorer James Bruce, who was Buffon's house guest
for a few weeks in 1774, led Buffon to change many small details
in his descriptions of the Abyssinians and other races of East
Africa, but not to alter the basic spirit of his earlier accounts.

Buffon's greatest failure as an anthropologist was his inability
to reach the concept of cultural relativity, though he often seemed
very close to it. Here again, an old idea, Natural Law, blocked
his way to a new idea. His overriding awareness of the oneness of
man, the constancy and unity of the human condition, his assumption of universal moral and cultural and esthetic absolutes, led
him to disregard not only what were truly superficial aspects of
the "varieties" of the human species, but real and important differences as well:

I don't believe that it is necessary for me to go into much detail concerning everything that relates to the customs of these savage nations
[American Indian]. All the authors who have written about them have
failed to note that what they have presented to us as fixed customs and
usages and as the mores of societies of men were in fact nothing more
than the particular actions of certain individuals, often determined
purely by circumstances, or by personal whim. Certain nations, they
tell us, eat their enemies; others burn them; still others mutilate them.
These are perpetually at war, while those seek to live in peace; among
these, fathers are killed when they reach a certain age, while among
those the fathers and mothers devour their own children. All these
stories, which the travelers have brought before us with so much complacency, are nothing more than so many accounts of particular facts,
and signify only that a certain savage has eaten his enemy, and that
another one burned or mutilated his, and that a third ate his own
infants. All these events may be found within a single nation of savages
as easily as among several nations, for every nation where there is neither
rule, nor law, nor master, nor generally respected customs, is less a
nation than a tumultuous assemblage of barbarous and lawless men,
who obey only their own individual passions, and who, having no concept of common interests, are incapable of directing themselves toward
a single goal, or of submitting to established custom, or of any behavior
at all that assumes a succession of rational designs approved by the
greater number. (H.N. III, "*Variétés dans l'Espèce Humaine*")

Because he underestimated the possibilities of human variability, Buffon could see little intrinsic interest in many of the facts he gathered about distant peoples. The customs of others are of interest only to the man who considers his own customs to be relative, not, in most cases, absolute norms from which all others have degenerated. Buffon felt, therefore, only too often a need to sustain his readers' interest by presenting the most exotic and "colorful" details he could find, and many sections of the *Histoire Naturelle de l'Homme* are consequently little more than catalogues of marvels and horrors. Reports, authenticated or unauthenticated, of human monsters, of men who were incredibly old, incredibly fat, incredibly small, or incredibly tall, were garnered with equal avidity. All the varieties of sexual mutilation were exhaustively inventoried; "One can imagine nothing bizarre or absurd of this nature," Buffon assured his readers, "that men somewhere have not put into practice, either through passion, or through superstition." (H.N. II, *"De l'Homme; De la Puberté"*) Even Buffon's hypertrophic sense of system and order could not always neatly channel this deluge of miscellany, and faint suggestions of gossip do sometimes linger in the air.

V *Buffon and the Proponents of Progress*

There are a series of letters in Buffon's extant correspondence addressed to an Abbé Dodun, extending from 1776 to 1782. They are business letters, but singularly chilling business letters. They are concerned with the details of the imprisonment of the Abbé de Saint-Belin, a brother of Buffon's late wife, imprisoned by the ecclesiastical authorities on a *lettre de cachet* obtained by Buffon. The Abbé de Saint-Belin, characterized in Buffon's letters to Dodun by such phrases as "that poor madman," "a bad head," "a bad sort," "our man," and "our wretched abbé," was guilty of no crime; he had many debts, and his irresponsibility in financial matters brought embarrassment upon his immediate family; he had appealed to Buffon, his brother-in-law, for help in finding "an asylum," only to discover, too late, and to his horror, that the price of the Count de Buffon's "protection" was the complete loss of his own freedom. In a letter of February 7, 1776, Buffon instructed Dodun, "In order to put an end to the ridiculous enterprises of the Abbé de Saint-Belin . . . keep the abbé inside his house, once he has entered it," and, in a letter of March 25, 1776, Buffon noted,

"He requests the liberty to take up his residence in another building . . . but M. Le Brun tells me that that might be dangerous." [9]

In Montbard, on November 2, 1772, a M. Nicolas-Dominique
Mandonnet, a municipal magistrate, protested during a meeting
of the town council against Buffon's attempt to obtain reimbursement for damages done to his property. Mandonnet's language
was rough and intemperate. "He is a terrible man," he said of
Buffon, "whose greed is so great that if he could ever come close
to the Eternal Father, he would grab his hat or his coat; he is a
tyrant, and a usurper." Buffon filed suit for defamation against
Mandonnet, and his correspondence contains letters, frank appeals to "influence," written to the *intendant* of the province ("I
ask your support and your counsels in this affair, in which my
reputation and my honor are at stake") and to an official of the
royal household ("Mandonnet must not be named magistrate
. . . this is the sole means of restoring peace in this little city,
where I have maintained it these past forty years; but, in a single
year, this man, who is some sort of madman, finding himself
magistrate, has stirred up all kinds of trouble. . . ."). On June 6,
1773, Buffon was able to write triumphantly to his *chère amie,*
Mme Daubenton, that Mandonnet was "to be a magistrate no
longer." [10]

In Paris, one rainy morning early in September, 1782, the monks
of the Abbey of Saint-Victor, who had refused to vacate a building Buffon wanted to demolish, as part of his plan for enlarging
the Jardin du Roi, awoke to find that Buffon's laborers were busily
ripping their roof off.[11]

Buffon's correspondence affords many similar examples of vic-
tims of arbitrary power wielded by Buffon, some fairly trivial, like
the rain-soaked monks of Saint-Victor, huddling in their beds, and
some not so trivial, like the frivolous and foolish Abbé de Saint-
Belin, walled up in his clerical prison, assailing a deaf ear with his
pathetic letters of protest. Buffon's identification with the power
structure of the *ancien régime* was total; it was not merely a
colorful façade, masking a covert but deep-seated liberalism.
Buffon was a man of power, real power; he sought it all of his life
with unflagging determination, and he seldom hesitated long in
deciding to use it against people who stood between him and his
goals.

From a historical perspective, the Enlightenment appears above all to have been a time of a new assertion of respect for the human spirit, a time when new doctrines of the rights of man were conceived and enunciated by a small circle of far-seeing men. Do the facts of Buffon's private life, his conformity, his ambition, and his ruthlessness, exclude him from the company of these men? Did he stand outside of the greatest intellectual movement of his time? Or did, in his case, actual practice and basic conviction simply point in opposite directions? These questions, like many others that have divided Buffon scholars, seem finally irresolvable, simply for lack of conclusive evidence. An authoritarian character and appetites, for example, are obviously not enough to exclude anyone from a circle centered around Voltaire, fully as avid a collector of titles and demolisher of enemies as Buffon himself. Nevertheless, Buffon's political position has been a subject for scholarly debate.

In 1919 Louis Dimier, an enthusiast for L'Action Française, attempted, in the chapter *"Buffon et l'Encyclopédie"* of his biography of Buffon, to establish Buffon as "one of the organs of the ancient authority," a staunch opponent of the Encyclopedists and the "upheaval of intellectual values" they represented.[12] In support of his case, Dimier painted the Encyclopedists as irresponsible anarchists, revolutionaries, and spreaders of the pollution of foreign ideas, positions which Buffon quite evidently could not have supported, and he described at length Buffon's quarrels with Condillac, Voltaire, and the encyclopedist D'Alembert. These quarrels did, in effect, take place, but they were intellectual and personal in nature, rather than ideological. Buffon and D'Alembert did repeatedly clash, over four decades, in both the Académie Royale des Sciences and the Académie Française, but the jejune power plays and academic political maneuvering they engaged in were motivated exclusively by mutual antipathy and mutual desire for dominance. As Henri Nadault de Buffon very aptly put it, "D'Alembert did not like Buffon . . . he found neither his person nor his talents sympathetic." [13] Moreover, during the early years of the *Encyclopédie,* Buffon was on friendly terms with both Diderot and Rousseau, its major writers. He went so far at one time as to promise Diderot an article on *Nature* for the *Encyclopédie.* The article was apparently never delivered, but Buffon's relations with both men remained cordial.[14] Claude-Adrien Helvétius, possibly the most politically radical of all the *philosophes,* was one of Buffon's most intimate personal friends, and Buffon was long a familiar figure at the *soirées* of the Baron d'Holbach, the group's most flagrant atheist.[15]

Buffon's relations with two American Enlightenment figures and "revolutionaries," Benjamin Franklin and Thomas Jefferson, were equally close. Franklin's papers on his experiments with lightning rods had been translated into French and published through Buffon's efforts,[16] and, during Franklin's longest stay in France, from 1776 to 1785, he and Buffon were so conspicuously friendly that several Frenchmen who sought favors from Buffon wrote to Franklin first to ask for his intercession.[17] Buffon and Jefferson were briefly engaged in a mild polemic over Buffon's assumption that the air of the New World promoted the rapid "degeneration" of species of all kinds, a notion that later made Buffon's name a favorite subject for denunciation in Fourth of July orations during the early years of the American Republic. Jefferson had challenged this assumption in his *Notes on Virginia,* which was published in France in 1785 during Jefferson's period of residence there as American envoy and ambassador. Jefferson's objections were couched, however, in terms so politic that not even Buffon could take offense: "and whilst I render every tribute of honor and esteem to the celebrated zoologist, who has added, and is still adding, so many precious things to the treasures of science, I must doubt whether in this instance he has not cherished error also, by lending her a moment his vivid imagination and bewitching language."[18] Buffon and Jefferson often dined together,[19] and, with Jefferson's help, Buffon obtained for the Cabinet du Roi hides of a panther, a deer, an elk, a reindeer, and a moose. Jefferson had also attempted to procure a mammoth's hide, convinced that at least a few of those massive beasts must still be alive somewhere in the vast American wilderness, but without success.[20]

Buffon did not permit even his celebrated quarrel with Voltaire to sour his relations with the *philosophes.* In 1774 there was an exchange of conciliatory letters, initiated by Buffon, and Buffon sent his eleven-year-old son to visit Voltaire at Ferney. With a supremely theatrical gesture, Voltaire solemnly seated the boy in his own armchair, like a visiting monarch, and stood before him with his head bared, in reverence to the representative of genius.[21]

Buffon's actual writings on the subject of the nature of society

shed perhaps even less light on his position than do his cordial-
but-distant or up-and-down relations with the leading *philosophes*.
He seldom wrote on social questions, and always in very specialized contexts. A few of his more explicit statements do have a dis-
turbingly authoritarian ring and are even at times suggestive of
advice to the husbandman on the care of blooded stock, but this is
neither very surprising nor very significant, since these passages
occur in essays that he had deliberately narrowed to deal only
with the purely physical half of his *homo duplex:*

A civilized people that lives in a certain comfort, accustomed to a life
that is regulated, gentle, and peaceful, and which is, through the efforts
of a good government, sheltered from certain miseries, never lacking
those things that are absolutely necessary, will be, for these reasons,
composed of men who are stronger, handsomer, and more graceful
than the people of nations that are savage and independent. . . .
(H.N. III, *"Variétés dans l'Espèce Humaine"*)

However, whatever political coloration one chooses to assign to
Buffon—and several distinctly different cases can be put together
—provision must always be made for an exceptionally high view
of human worth. Buffon's fundamental attitude toward human
nature was summed up in the question: *"Pourquoi l'avilir mal à
propos?"* Why take an ignoble view of human nature when there
is no reason to do so? (H.N. II, *"De la Nature de l'Homme"*)
And human society, he always insisted, was a product of the
rational half of his *homo duplex,* an achievement of reason, distinguished from animal societies precisely by its capacity to reach
higher and higher levels of perfection. Little more was needed in
ancien régime France to make a man a dangerous radical.

CHAPTER 9

"Le Style Est L'Homme Même"

I *Buffon's Literary Theories*

T. S. ELIOT, in a discussion of the standards by which one may determine with respect to a given piece of writing "whether it is literature or not," included Buffon in a short list of writers whose works are treated as literature on the basis of their possessing "a gift of language which makes them delightful to read to all those who can enjoy language well written, even if they are unconcerned with the objects which the writers had in view." [1] If this is an adequate criterion, there should be little question as to Buffon's literary status. Important French critics and writers of both the eighteenth and nineteenth centuries— Rousseau, Baudelaire, Sainte-Beuve—used superlatives freely in praising his prose style. Emile Faguet actually named him, on the basis of some prose passages of marked lyric intensity (for Buffon wrote no verse), as one of the three major French poets of the latter part of the eighteenth century.[2] But the mere fact that a scientific writer's prose may be "delightful to read" is a very fragile basis for regarding him as a master of imaginative writing and an important literary figure. It would seem to many that the prose must be demonstrably literary in some deeper sense. Buffon himself was deeply concerned with questions of this nature, and his own discussions of literature suggest that he would not have been content with Eliot's indulgent view—even though it is almost entirely on the basis of such views that critics and literary historians have traditionally regarded Buffon as a literary figure. Buffon was the author of one of the most widely known and most often quoted essays on the nature of literary style to be published during the eighteenth century—an essay that set forth in some detail his own criteria of literary value and, in effect, defined and defended his own literary position—and it seems appropriate to begin a discussion of the nature of his style with a brief consideration of this essay.

Le Discours sur le Style, as the piece has come to be known, was the oration Buffon delivered before the Académie Française on the occasion of his formal reception into that body on August 25, 1753. This essay contains his final thoughts on style—he reprinted it without major changes in 1777 in the fourth volume of the *Suppléments* to the *Histoire Naturelle,* and in 1785 he affirmed his continued adherence to its views in conversations with Hérault de Séchelles—but despite the essay's fame, it is not itself typical of Buffon's best writing. It was written somewhat more hastily than Buffon usually chose to work. He entered the Académie Française as the replacement for the recently deceased Archbishop of Sens, but his election was an afterthought on the part of the academy, pushed through in an unusually short time, many of the traditional preliminaries dispensed with, when the government unexpectedly rejected the first candidate proposed by the academy, the playwright and poet Alexis Piron. Buffon's *discours de réception,* the product of less than two months' work, was a brilliant success, but, as generations of *lycéens* who were obliged to learn it by heart came to know, it was not a faultless piece. It was studded with striking aphorisms and memorable phrases, but it also contained more than a few resounding but rather vague platitudes. The passages of fulsome flattery addressed to Buffon's new *confrères,* obligatory features of a *discours de réception,* were imperfectly absorbed, and this is symptomatic of the essay's major flaw: it was far from consistent throughout—the gravest of shortcomings according to Buffon's own theories.

Buffon began by promising his audience "no more than your own goods," "a few ideas on style derived from your writings; it is in reading you, in admiring you, that they have been conceived." This promise, of a sort of reasoned defense of generally accepted neoclassical practices, was only partially fulfilled. Only on questions of diction did Buffon show himself resolutely conservative. Few of his contemporaries could have been as content as Buffon with the limitations imposed in this area. He denounced writers of "cultivated but sterile wit" who have "corrupted the language by wrenching words from their accepted use," and those too who disdain all but the most subtle thoughts, thoughts that are "like a leaf of hammered metal, acquiring luster at the ex-

pense of substance." All purely verbal ingenuity he found suspect:
"Nothing is more opposed to natural beauty than effort expended
in depicting ordinary and common things in pretentious and
extraordinary terms; nothing is more degrading to the writer; far
from admiring him, one pities him for having devoted so much
time to creating new combinations of syllables that convey no
new idea." Gratuitous ornamentation, such as that obtained
through the abuse of antithesis, "those sparks sprung from the
forced collisions of words," were to Buffon only one more sign of
a writer's complacent and uncritical admiration of his own clever-
ness. It is interesting to note, however, that in defending a restrictive diction Buffon contrived at the same time, with his allusions
to metal foil and electric sparks, to demonstrate that the "New
Science" offered to the writer a wealth of opportunities for renew-
ing the shopworn stock of neoclassical imagery. Buffon's advice
to "name things only by the most general terms" must be balanced
against the importance he attached to imagery: "if one can add
beauty of coloring to energy of design, if one can, in a word,
represent each idea by a lively and well-defined image, and shape
each succession of ideas into a single vision that is harmonious
and moving, the tone will be, not merely lofty, but sublime."

Paradoxically, Buffon expressed his approval of his new colleagues' diction not by direct praise but by attacks upon the
mistakes of unnamed figures. More than a third of this essay,
suavely introduced as a detailing of the successful techniques of
these colleagues, consists of such attacks. Moreover, even more
inconsistently, many of the unnamed figures attacked are easily
identified as members of the very academy he was addressing. To
make the point inescapable Buffon actually added an explanatory
note in 1777 in which he specifically identified Montesquieu's
Esprit des Lois as the work he had in mind in his strictures
against choppy writing produced by too frequent subdivisions.
His indignant comments on the ostentatious display of wit were
just as evidently intended for Voltaire. He did not openly express
his aversion to poetry—often propounded in private conversations
—before this assembly of poets and poetasters he had come to
praise, but he did go so far as to suggest that the writing of
poetry was simply a matter of "mechanical" imitation, requiring
no more than "a fairly good ear," and that its sole purpose was to
produce "exaggerated" pictures of men and nature.

But the most striking of all the inconsistencies that one encounters in this supposedly objective account of the style of an entire age is its preoccupation with the stylistic procedures of one man—Buffon himself. Throughout the *discours de réception* the style that is praised is the style of the *Histoire Naturelle*. This is immediately apparent in the initial assumption that the basic unit of prose is not the phrase, the sentence, or the paragraph, but the essay, and that the essay can be no other than the presentation of a tightly interconnected set of ideas. The first of the great aphorisms that won the *discours* its fame reflects this point of view: "Style is no more than the order and the movement that one puts into one's ideas." This "order and movement" are the result of a long meditation upon the subject. Prolonged contemplation of each component idea permits the writer to single out those that are the most basic and to discover the essential interrelations that will guide his presentation. Buffon, apparently, could conceive of no other approach. Spontaneity is always a vice. Only faults can spring from the neglect of this first effort at thinking through a subject:

It is for this reason that those who write as they speak, though they may speak well, write badly; that those who abandon themselves to the first fires of their imagination adopt a tone they cannot sustain; that those who fear to lose isolated, fugitive thoughts and who write short detached sections at different times never succeed in pulling them together without forced transitions; that, in a word, there are so many works composed of disparate fragments and so few that have been fused together into a single stream.

In insisting upon the primacy of the plan, in reducing the essence of literary style to the "order and movement" imposed on the ideas presented, Buffon affirmed his conviction that literature can only be the expression of fully controlled intellectual activity. This view is obviously highly restrictive. While admitting Buffon's own work, it excludes much that we normally regard as literary. The neoclassical theorist assumes a position diametrically opposed to such popular modern views as Sigmund Freud's celebrated definition of an artist:

The artist is orginally a man who turns from reality because he cannot come to terms with the demand for the renunciation of instinctual satis-

faction as it is first made, and who then in phantasy-life allows full
play to his erotic and ambitious wishes . . . with his special gifts he
moulds his phantasies into a new kind of reality. . . .[3]

Buffon's view strips literature also of its privileged status, of all
overtones of godlike creativity. It becomes just another form of
human endeavor. "If the sources of style, as Buffon says, are order
and movement," noted General Charles de Gaulle, "the same is
true of politics."[4]

The creative writer, Buffon insists, must imitate nature, whose
productions achieve perfection "because she works according to
an eternal plan, from which she never departs." The human mind,
though it "can create nothing," can "lift itself by contemplation
to the level of the most sublime truths." The writer's value is to be
measured by the extent of his insight into the essential form of
things. It is in this context that the most famous aphorism of the
discours de réception must be understood: "The style is the man
himself; style therefore cannot be stripped away, cannot be carried off, cannot change." What was most important to Buffon in
the "order and movement" arrived at through long and painful
meditation was that they reflected a particular mind, and, as they
were to some extent peculiarly personal, they might serve as the
basis for the perpetual fame of an individual. One man's vision,
perfectly articulated, assures immortality. There is no possibility
of a dichotomy between form and content in Buffon's theory.
Form is itself the most important aspect of content:

A beautiful style is such, in effect, only by the infinite number of truths
it presents. All of the intellectual beauties it contains, all of the relationships of which it is composed, are so many truths, as useful—and perhaps more precious to man's understanding—as those that may make
up the essence of the subject treated.

The very choice of a subject is a crucial mark of personal genius:
"If one has penetrated to the most general of all ideas, if the
object is, in itself, great, the tone will be seen to lift itself to the
same heights." Buffon's selection of "natural philosophy" as his
field, which today seems a bizarre choice for a writer with hopes
of eternal literary fame, was thus an inevitable consequence of
his belief that science had, in his time, advanced to the point at

which it could finally elucidate all the mysteries of existence, everything that had puzzled or frightened or awed mankind through the centuries. His confidence in his destiny as a writer was in part an expression of his faith in science.

In the Romantic era the aphorism "The style is the man," taken out of context, was often cited in justification of excessive eccentricities of style, in defense of the right of the individual to develop to the full his most bizarre idiosyncrasies. Yet, throughout this passage, Buffon studiously maintained a generality of tone that effectively blocks any such interpretation. Phrases like "the man" and "the writer" evoke only general representatives of humanity. To Buffon, a writer's value was not in the atypicality of his emotions, but in the efficiency and completeness of his intellectual formation, the least idiosyncratic of the components of his being. It may even be argued that the line properly means "style *is* man, style is the essence of humanness, the foremost human trait." A mastery of style thus assures the personal fame of a particular author precisely because it is one of those universal intellectual qualities that make possible one man's effective communication with others; it is a guarantee that his vision of things, his insights, will not be lost. To interpret the formula as meaning that a writer can be recognized, judged, and categorized by peculiarities in his manner of expressing himself is equally irrelevant to Buffon's intended meaning. In an extant early version of the *discours* he had specifically ruled out this view: "A great writer must have no distinguishing trait; the mark everywhere of the same pen, in diverse productions, reveals a lack of genius." [5] Yet, however unintentionally, Buffon did create a maxim that pithily suggests something of the immense complexity of the concept of style, its deep roots in the mystery of personal identity, and the maxim has acquired a life of its own, independent of its author's original intent, with its insistence on the purely intellectual character of style.

Buffon's was no coldly impersonal theory of literature, however. He did not neglect the role of the passions—merely firmly subordinated them to the intellect. Once the writer has discovered the plan he will follow, the plan that lies in the nature of things, "he will be anxious to give it body, he will have only pleasure in writing; ideas will come, one after another, easily, unforced, and the style will be natural and unlabored; the warmth born of his enthusiasm will inform the whole and will impart life to every expression used." Lyricism is admitted, but it is, in the phrase of Jacques Roger, an "intellectual lyricism." [6] The apparent platitudes that vie for attention with the great aphorisms in the *discours* are no less weighted with intended content. Such dubious gems as "One must act upon the soul and touch the heart while addressing the intellect" reflect Buffon's conviction that successful intellectual activity is charged with emotion. Much in the *discours* that appears to be a condemnation of the expression of emotion is in truth only a rejection of facile emotionalism, an affirmation of the need for restraint: "Finally, if one writes as one thinks, if one is fully convinced of the truth of that which one hopes to persuade others to accept, this personal integrity, which shows itself outwardly as tact toward others and recognizable authenticity in the style, will produce all its effect, provided that personal conviction does not manifest itself in too strong an enthusiasm, and that there is always more candor than complacency, more reason than heat." The *discours* opens with a denunciation of demagogues who have mastered the vulgar art of exciting the raw emotions of the masses. Buffon's distrust of effects that are easily achieved, even by unschooled authors who lack "the wisdom that is the product of a long practice of the art of writing," was a form of tribute to what he conceived to be the quality of his readers, "the small number of those whose intellect is sturdy, whose taste is discerning, and whose senses are exquisitely refined." A style appropriate to addressing a truly cultivated reader, he believed, must be concerned primarily with clearly expressed ideas. Buffon's *Discours sur le Style*, though some of its precepts are still, and even universally, valid, is "dated" in that it reflects throughout the literary situation of the French Enlightenment. It is a prescription for literary success only in an age that is truly intoxicated with ideas.

II   *Rhetoric and Logic Linked*

Some of the most important features of Buffon's style can be adequately illustrated in translated passages. This is possible because of the nature of his diction and the kind of clarity he sought in his writing. The diction, in accord with the views expounded in the *Discours*, was, whenever the subject permitted, formal and general, firmly delimited by the tenets of neoclassical taste, no words having been "wrenched from their accepted use." The clarity aimed at can be labeled "paraphrasable": he did not judge a passage to be "clear" until the written paraphrases of a number of readers, usually his assistants or his friends, were in agreement on all particulars. Quite appropriately, the absence of any trace of ambiguity was established by experimentation. One may find, therefore, many passages in Buffon's writings in which the series of choices that the translator must make, the choices that constitute the translator's art, are almost all virtually inevitable. This is not true, of course, of the greater part of his writing for Buffon's peculiar genius, like that of any other notable stylist, is often manifested in a very subtle choice between two apparent synonyms, or an unexpected, seemingly inexplicable choice that proves mysteriously apt, but it is true of enough passages to permit a discussion of his style to be illustrated, with some profit, by translated passages.[7]

The possibilities for straightforward translation without significant distortion in the style of a passage are particularly good in the introductory essays devoted to the exposition of general principles which begin all of the major divisions of the *Histoire Naturelle*. Moreover, Buffon's reputation as a master of traditional rhetoric is founded in great measure on these essays, though they make up a relatively small part of the great bulk of his writing. They contain some of the finest examples of classic Ciceronian periods to be found in the prose of the modern era, as the following "sentence" from the essay "Animaux Sauvages" (H.N. VI), illustrates:

We shall now see nature striding as sovereign across the land, sharing her domain with the animals, assigning to each one its particular element, climate and substance: we shall now see her in the forests, in the waters, on the plains, pronouncing her simple but immutable laws, impressing upon each species its inalterable character, and distributing with equity her gifts, compensating both good and evil; giving to some strength and courage, accompanied by need and voracity; to others, gentleness, temperance, and lightness of body, along with fear, anxiety and timidity; to all, liberty and constant habits, firm customs; to all, desire and physical love that is always easy to satisfy, and always followed by a fortunate fecundity.

The devices of classical rhetoric were designed to produce prose which was impressively ornate but which, at the same time, could be followed with ease by either a listener or a reader. Prose that was intended primarily to be declaimed or read aloud could involve no Proustian tangles, no verbs in search of a subject, nothing that required extraordinary concentration on the part of an audience. A periodic sentence is long and carefully wrought, but in no real sense complicated. It was unquestionably as aids to lucidity, a function reinforced by their familiarity to the reader, that the traditional rhetorical devices appealed to Buffon. In the sentence quoted above, for example, he personifies "nature," hardly a stroke of great originality, but in so doing he avoids the difficult problem of attaching a precise label to mysterious life forces, a label that might prove offensive to orthodox readers and censors as well as to amateurs of science suspicious of "systems"; he scrupulously employs the typically neoclassical organizational principles of antithesis and balance, but they prove singularly appropriate in a description of nature's own principle of compensation. This sentence illustrates the use of conventional techniques of exposition, but not at the expense of clarity in the presentation of subject matter; rather, much of its clarity can be attributed to the skillful use of the rhetorical devices, their total appropriateness.

Sentences this harmonious seem to the modern reader out of place in descriptions of natural processes he knows to be mysterious and chaotic, but to Buffon nature was above all basically harmonious. The style of his prose reflects his fundamental conviction of the reasonableness of nature. It was no accident that he chose to renew his inspiration, not by hiking into the rough hills around Montbard, but rather by strolling, elegantly attired, in a formal garden, created at great expense for that specific purpose.

He could employ both rhetoric and logic that dealt in neat divisions into categories and subcategories according to general principles because he believed in the reality of such divisions in nature itself. It was, again, no accident that his explanations of the nature of biological species constantly reminded his readers, and with cause, of Plato or Pliny. He could, like the ancient philosopher-scientists, solve problems by detailing all possible solutions and then selecting the "most reasonable" one, because he could conceive of no other order of things. The style of his prose, as well as its content, testifies to his affinity to the deists (not the atheists) of his time—to those to whom the presence of a creator was conjectural but the existence of an intelligent and intelligible world plan beyond all doubt.

III   *Lace Cuffs and Bonhomie*

Of all the many objectionable anecdotes concerning his great-granduncle that Nadault de Buffon reported in the notes to his *Correspondance de Buffon*, the one that evidently irritated him the most was the *"mauvaise plaisanterie"* of the Prince of Monaco to the effect that Buffon "could write only with his hands floating in lace cuffs." [8] The remark nevertheless became and has remained famous, and Buffon's *"manchettes de dentelle"* are an inseparable part of his public image, and not without reason, for the prince's gibe sums up pithily the most common hostile criticism of Buffon's style: that he was incapable of simplicity, a helpless prisoner of his own boundless thirst for elegance and grandeur. Much the same point is made by Voltaire's *"Dans un style ampoulé parlez-nous de physique"* [9] and Marmontel's observation that Buffon could be accused of having written "opulently in a genre that admits only a simple and natural style." [10] Condillac, the arch anti-Buffonian, put the matter the most bluntly, accusing Buffon of habitually "substituting for the most exact term the one that makes the most extravagant impression." [11]

Even the comments of Buffon's admirers occasionally reflect this view, as for example Rivarol's judgment that Buffon's style could best be described as "the manner of Bossuet applied to natural history," [12] since Bossuet is best known for his funeral orations, certainly the most flamboyantly unrestrained and ornate of literary genres. And the poet Lebrun's "Ode to M. de Buffon on his Detractors" could have done little to discomfit Buffon's enemies with such lines as: "For if you fear the tyranny / Of a monster jealous and perverse / Let fall the scepter of Genius, / Cease to flood the universe with light. / Descend from the heights of your soul, / Lower your wings of flame, / Break your sublime brushes, / Take the envious for models, / And with their treacherous varnish / Darken your gleaming canvasses." [13]

One of the most famous of these "gleaming canvasses," passages in which Buffon, to the delight of his most devoted readers, flourished his lace cuffs and launched into the "high style," was the description of the desert in the article on the camel (H.N. XI), a description in which, in the simplest of terms—for Buffon's notorious "general terms" are for the most part nothing more than words that are immediately familiar to everybody, words that directly and unequivocally affect every reader in the same way— he majestically evokes a sense of the enormous world of eight-eenth-century man, a world it took two years to sail around, a world in which distant places had not yet been banalized by technicolor travelogue films and in which the exotic and remote had to be pictured in the mind's eye with minimal assistance from written accounts and amateurish penciled sketches, a world, in fact, in which the words "exotic" and "remote" still had meaning:

Try to imagine a country without greenery and without water, a burn-ing sun, a sky always dry, sandy plains, mountains more arid still, over which the eye sweeps in vain and sight is lost without once fixing upon a living object; a dead land, as though stripped bare by the hot wind, offering to the eye only the remnants of bones, scattered stones, out-croppings of rock, upright or fallen, a desert without secrets in which no traveler has ever drawn a breath in the shade, or found a companion, or anything to remind him of living nature: absolute solitude, a thousand times more terrifying than that of the dense forests, for trees are other beings, other life, to the man who sees himself alone; more isolated, more naked, more lost, in these empty and limitless lands, he stares into space, on all sides, space that is like a tomb; the light of day, more melancholy than the shadows of night, is reborn only to shine upon his nakedness and impotence, to let him see more clearly the horror of his situation, driving back the boundaries of the void, extending around him the abyss of the immensity that separates him from the land of men, an immensity that he will attempt in vain to cross, for hunger, thirst, and the scorching heat press upon every moment that remains between despair and death.

Dramatic and graphic passages in the article on the lion (H.N. IX) were also much admired:

Wounds irritate them, but without frightening them; they are not even discouraged by the sight of vast numbers of enemies: a single one of these lions of the wilderness will often attack an entire caravan; and when, after a violent and stubborn struggle, they sense themselves weakening, instead of fleeing, they fight on in retreat, always facing the foe, never once turning their backs.

Yet one need not read far in the *Histoire Naturelle* to dispel
the impression that its tone is monotonously stentorian or op-
pressively "magnificent." In fact, though Buffon could ascend to
oratorical heights when it seemed appropriate, the most notable
difference between the greater part of his prose and that of his
most eminent contemporaries is its general affability of tone. Unquestionably one of the most pompous men of his time in his
public life, in his prose Buffon never addressed his reader *de haut
en bas*. The tone he adopted most often was that of the *causeur
de salon*, the tone of the drawing room, formal but never distant
or cold, never truculent or hectoring—the tone of a man of the
world among his peers, confident of the sympathy, and even the
warm friendship of his audience.

This pervasive affability is most apparent in the descriptive
articles on individual animals, and it does much to explain why
they were so popular in their own day and why excerpts from
them could later be used to make up children's books. It must
be noted too, however, that frankly prurient interest in Buffon's
richly detailed descriptions of the *"amours"* of animals and birds
—sections usually missing in the nineteenth-century children's
editions—contributed substantially to the popular success of the
Histoire Naturelle. These passages, although based on precise
observation, are never coldly clinical. They are frankly evaluative.
Confronted with any manifestations of the boundless mystery of
sexual love, Buffon was always primarily the moral philosopher:

There are few birds as ardent, as powerful in love as the sparrow;
they have been seen to couple as many as twenty times in succession,
always with the same eagerness, the same trepidation, the same expression of pleasure; and, strange to say, the female seems to grow
impatient first with a game that ought to tire her less than the male,
but it can please her also much less, for there are no preliminaries, no
caresses, no variety to the thing; much petulance without tenderness,
movements always hasty, indicative only of a need to be satisfied for
its own sake. Compare the loves of the pigeon to those of the sparrow,
and you shall see almost all the nuances that extend from the physical
to the moral. (H.N.O. III, *"Le Moineau"*)

. . . tender caresses, soft movements, timid kisses, that become intimate and urgent only at the moment of enjoyment; this moment even,
brought back within seconds by new desires, new approaches equally

nuanced; an ardor ever durable, a taste ever constant, and, a still greater benefit, the power to satisfy them repeatedly, without end; no bad temper, no disgust, no quarrel; an entire lifetime devoted to the service of love and to the care of its fruits. . . . (H.N.O. II, *"Le Pigeon"*)

Buffon was unfailing in his efforts to "humanize" the descriptive articles, to maintain constantly some connection between the subject at hand and the personal concerns of his readers. He might, for example, apply to animals or birds terms usually applied only to humans, a device that delights children and exasperates adults, though Buffon often had little choice in the matter, owing both to the undeveloped state of the vocabulary of natural history in his day and the narrowness of neoclassical views on the propriety of terms. But the "humanizing" of his subjects was never a matter of vocabulary alone, but more a matter of profound sympathy, as can be seen in his account of the tame beaver sent to him from French Canada:

One day he escaped and descended by a cellar stair into the caverns of the old quarries that are under the Jardin du Roi. He fled a long way, swimming in the rank water on the bottoms of the caverns; nevertheless, as soon as he saw the light of the torches that I had brought there in the search for him, he came to those who were calling him and let himself be taken without trouble. He is friendly without being affectionate or caressing, his requests are made through a little plaintive cry or a few gestures of the hand; as soon as someone gives him a morsel of food, he carries it off and hides himself to eat it at his leisure. He sleeps a great deal, resting on his stomach; he will eat almost anything, except meat, which he steadfastly refuses, cooked or raw: he gnaws away at everything that comes in his way, cushions, furniture, or trees; and the barrel in which he was shipped had to be reinforced with sheets of tin. (H.N. VIII)

Often Buffon managed to endue an apparently straightforward account of animal behavior with some quality of human drama, even tragedy:

. . . a female wolf I kept three years, although shut up alone while still quite young in a large pen with a mastiff of the same age, was not able to accustom herself to living with him, nor to submit to him, even when she was in heat. Although the weaker, she was the more aggressive and bad tempered; she provoked, she attacked, she nipped and bit the dog, who at first was content to defend himself, but finally throttled her. (H.N. VII)

Another "humanizing" device frequently employed was the broadly philosophical observation on the affairs of men—and animals—casually inserted into a technical discussion that had somehow called it to mind. In the midst of his explanation of the necessary role of the predator in the balance of nature, for example, Buffon remarks, "Let us admit nevertheless that the motive that drives man to question, to doubt this usage, does honor to humanity," and promptly plunges into a digression on "pity." Interpolations of this nature were much less startling to Buffon's contemporaries than they are to the modern reader, for the tradition of the fable and the bestiary, the habit of looking for moral lessons in natural phenomena, now more remote than any other feature of ancient literature, still had its practitioners in the eighteenth century. Buffon was, of course, no fabulist, but animals and birds never emerge from his descriptions as Cartesian automatons. Though they are often driven by forces beyond their control or understanding, their behavior patterns remain distinctive, and their actions often seem to involve something very like conscious choice. He sought above all in these articles to capture what he called the "nature" of the animal, and this somewhat mystic concept involved, primarily, a definite physical constitution, a process of adaptation to a particular environment, and a "personality," shared by all of the members of a particular species.

Buffon's vocabulary may at times strike a modern naturalist as unnecessarily quaint and his view of animal "nature" as naïve, but his procedures marked, nevertheless, a substantial advance over the practices of both his predecessors and his contemporaries. His descriptive articles have considerable charm, but their liveliness did not represent any sacrifice of scientific objectivity, to the extent that it was attainable in Buffon's day. Here again the author of the *Histoire Naturelle* managed to enjoy the best of both worlds.

IV *Striving for Severity*

In 1962 in the introduction to his critical edition of Buffon's *Epoques de la Nature* (H.N.S. V, 1778), based on some surviving manuscript versions, Jacques Roger discussed the style of that essay in some detail.[14] With the exception of the introductory passages, actually written to be delivered publicly as part of a formal academic oration, Roger found that the essay's style departed markedly from the precepts of the *Discours sur le Style* and its overriding preoccupation with such qualities as nobility, sublimity, and grandeur. He labeled much of this late essay's style "exclusively didactic" and noted: "Examination of changes made in the manuscripts confirms the impression drawn from the published version. The author did not hesitate to write 'heavy' sentences in his efforts to express an idea as precisely as possible." In the *Epoques,* Roger observed, Buffon "used technical terms whenever he had need of them," and in such technical passages he achieved "extreme simplicity of style," particularly with regard to the sentence structure and the "solidly constructed" paragraphs. Most significantly, "there is no striving for rhythmic effects."

The alterations in Buffon's style noted by Roger are symptomatic of general changes in the character of eighteenth-century science and of Buffon's efforts toward the end of his career to come to terms with these changes. The day of the elegant amateur was passing and the professional scientist, the technocrat, was making his appearance. Science was slowly acquiring that vast burden of technology that would soon effectively bar access to all but the trained specialist. Detailed monographs on minute aspects of minute problems were increasingly the fashion. Systems, more now than ever before, were suspect. Buffon, his fortune made and the popularity of his work with the general public long a *fait accompli,* was, to judge from changes in the tone of his writing in the 1770's and 1780's, primarily concerned at that time with maintaining his scientific respectability and with winning the approbation of the earnest, unimaginative young men who were beginning to dominate the academies.

The *Histoire Naturelle des Minéraux* (1783–88), the last massive block in the structure, is the section of the *Histoire Naturelle* in which this apparent effort at toning down, at converting Buffon's gloriously literary style into something very much like a superior variety of scientific prose, is most in evidence. Stylistically, however, these final writings are of interest primarily because the fundamental features of Buffon's style resisted all change and are thrown into high relief in their new, soberer surroundings. Nevertheless, Buffon did succeed in the *Histoire Naturelle des Minéraux* in producing a passable counterfeit of standard scientific prose. The five volumes of this section rely heavily on lengthy quotations, and, in the absence of punctuation, it would often be difficult to tell where a particular quoted passage ended and Buffon's prose began again.

Never before had Buffon's prose carried so heavy a freight of factual data. In every article of the five volumes the facts pile up, heavier and more stubborn than those of the earlier volumes, dominating and transforming the tone: where in the world mineral X is found, with names of the travelers who have seen it there, how, according to Buffon, the deposits were first laid down, with brief accounts and refutations of the erroneous theories of other savants, the physical and chemical properties of mineral X —weight, density, refractive qualities, solubility, fusibility, inflammability—ways of extracting it, ways to use it, and so on and so forth, with indefatigable thoroughness. If by nothing else, the reader is overwhelmed, stunned to admiration, by the sheer weight of the factual knowledge acquired by the elderly Buffon, his organizing ability, his insatiable curiosity, his boundless ingenuity in explaining away anomalies. For the most part, in presenting these facts, Buffon employed the least complicated structures and forms—simple declarative sentences (sometimes in conglomerates), verbs in the indicative ("Abbé Rochon brought back from that island a large and beautiful two-pointed needle of this crystal; one may see it in the King's Collection" (H.N.M. III, *"Des Stalactites Cristallisées du Quartz"*). And, particularly in the last volumes, there is a marked increase in the *Histoire Naturelle des Minéraux* of short, choppy articles, dictionarylike articles that make the reader uncomfortably aware that the highly readable *Histoire Naturelle* is after all, at bottom, a reference work, the most unreadable of genres. The affable social tone too veers decidedly toward the dryly serious; the cultivated amateur is still obviously a part of the intended audience, but more of the solemn dedication of the true initiate is now demanded of him.

But all of this, this methodical inventory of the earth's surface, is only one aspect of the style of the *Histoire Naturelle des Minéraux*, the most conspicuous, the least important. Buffon the mineralogist was no plodding rock hound, no data-grubbing field worker; he remained the untraveled thinker, the *savant de cabinet*,

the man of visions, the man with a system. And when, like
a sounding whale, the system suddenly surfaces, as it does in
article after article of the *Histoire Naturelle des Minéraux*, the
style ceases to be "exclusively didactic."

The system itself is simple, and can be stated either in a
straightforward declarative sentence—"There is in nature only
one single original force, and that's the reciprocal attraction between all parts of matter" (H.N.M. V, *"Traité de l'Aimant, article
premier"*—or, viewed as a cycle, in a suitably rhythmic circular
sentence,

Such then is the origin of the diverse forces, general as well as particular, of which we have just spoken. Attraction, acting in a sense contrary
to its direction, produced impulsion, from the very first moment matter
existed: this impulsion brought into existence the element of fire, which
produced electricity; and we shall see that magnetism is only a particular modification of that general electricity, which wavers in its
course toward iron-bearing matter. (H.N.M. V, *"Traité de l'Aimant,
article premier"*)

But there is purpose in Buffon's constant references to his system;
it is not simply dragged in out of habit, an aging gentleman's
idée fixe. He aimed at nothing less than the total validation of
his system. He had to demonstrate that it did in fact explain
everything, every earthly phenomenon, biological, geological,
chemical, or physical. The *Histoire Naturelle* was not only *"générale"* but also *"particulière."* The theory had to mesh with the facts,
completely, universally, and Buffon, despite his metaphysician's
taste for absolute statements, had too much respect for the facts,
was too good a practical scientist, to make this an easy task.
Again and again the facts proved recalcitrant, and whenever this
happened, particularly when the conflict involved an opposing
view of things offered by rival savants, Buffon's free flowing style
became suddenly complex. All the resources of the man of letters
were then called into play; the scientist gave way to the agile
polemicist, the creator of extraordinary images. A close look at
many paragraphs in the *Histoire Naturelle des Minéraux*, in the
midst of what appears to be barren technical exposition, will reveal a miniature courtroom drama. Lightly concealed beneath the
sobriety of the tone, the mass of technical terms, there are blatant
appeals to emotion—indignation, admiration, awe, pity, and con-

tempt—insidious plays on words, and in the end, offered in lieu of balanced arguments and complete evidence, there are highly animated pictures, projections of Buffon's imagination:

Some recent naturalists, and among others Linnaeus and his pupils, have claimed, quite inappropriately, that stone crystals owe their configuration to the salts: we shall not stop to refute opinions so ill founded. Nevertheless all competent physicists, and notably the learned mineralogist Cronstedt, have denied, and with good reason, that the salts have any part in the formation, much less the configuration, of these crystals; it is sufficient, he says, to note that there exist metallic bodies that form crystals through fusion, to demonstrate that the configuration of crystals is not dependent upon salts. That is very certain; salts and stone crystals have nothing in common other than the faculty to form crystals, a faculty that is more than common, since it belongs to all matter, not only saline, but stone, or even metal, from the moment these substances are brought to the liquid state, whether by water, or by fire, because, in this state of liquidity, the particles that are similar are able to approach one another and to join together through the sole force of attraction, and to form, by their groupings, crystals whose form depends upon the primitive shapes of their constituent parts, and upon the arrangements which these thin layers take among themselves, by virtue of their mutual and reciprocal affinity. (H.N.M. III, *"Des Stalactites Cristallisées du Quartz"*)

But even when Buffon was not mustering the forces of eloquence in defense of his system, he did not write precisely like an ordinary scientist. For one thing, his concerns were much broader, much more humanistic; even minerals and metals were of interest to him primarily in relation to man, as components of man's environment. The article on gold (H.N.M. II), for example —"metal that will lose its nobility only when men themselves become noble, having won through to a wisdom that is now no more than a very distant prospect"—was for Buffon the occasion for a passionate denunciation of Spain's gold-oriented colonial policy in the New World, both on economic ("it has served only to debase the value of our own stores of gold") and humanitarian grounds ("What a difference for nature and for humanity if the myriad wretches who have perished in those tunnels deep in the bowels of the earth, had been able to employ the strength of their limbs in the cultivation of its surface! they would have transformed the wild and primitive appearance of their undevel-

oped lands into orderly, plowed fields, smiling countrysides, as
fecund as they were sterile, and are still. . . ."), and the article
on iron (H.N.M. II) was the occasion for a detailed and bitterly
indignant critique of the taxes imposed on foundry operations in
France, an iniquitous spider web spun by ignorance that was
strangling the very industry upon which France's future greatness
depended (and also Buffon's private fortune).

His outspoken aversion to the proliferation of technical terms
and to the systematic approach to nomenclature he felt to be
responsible for it also separated him from his scientific colleagues:
"Nothing has more retarded the progress of the sciences than this
logomachia, this creation of new words. . . ." (H.N.M. II, *"Du
Soufre"*); "Such is the defect in all methodological nomenclatures,
they vanish, their inadequacy exposed, as soon as one tries to
apply them to the real objects of nature" (H.N.M. II, *"Des Sels"*).
In the age of Lavoisier, Buffon clung stubbornly to the four elements of the Greeks: earth, air, fire, and water. Sulfur, he insisted, was nothing more than "the element of fire fixed by acid,"
and acid itself simply "the combination of fire and air." His affinity, in spite of all his efforts to keep abreast of the relentless on-
ward surge of science, to master the new discoveries and theories,
was still to the ancient Greek philosopher-scientist; the kind of
lucidity he valued was not possible in a world in which there
truly existed a multiplicity of things, swarms of intractable data
that "oppose the free operation of the intellect, weighing it down
with petty points of detail" (H.N.M. II, *"Des Sels"*).

The diction he preferred, in earth science as well as in zoology
or ornithology, was one that facilitated the creation of images
and the establishing of evident analogies: "The primitive fire was
the *fluid* in which took place the crystallization of feldspar and
schorl. . . ." (H.N.M. III, *"Stalactites Vitreuses"*); "We cannot
therefore doubt that the power of electricity was acting with
complete freedom and causing violent explosions in the *cavities*
or *blisters* produced near the earth's surface by the primitive fire"
(H.N.M. V, *"Traité de l'Aimant, article premier"*). His diction
often suggests that he was thinking in terms of scale models (e.g.,
"blisters"), and it encourages the reader, who *sees* as he reads, in
manageable images, to conclude that he has in fact understood
the processes described. The diction preferred by his colleagues,
systematic and arcane, evocative only of abstract categories, was

better calculated to intimidate the average reader; it was a medium for the exchange of specialized information among specialists, and as such hostile to "general terms," and this Buffon's prose never was, never could be.

What was perhaps the most basic of the differences between Buffon's use of language and that of rival contemporary scientists, his refusal to confine speculative ratiocination within rigidly defined limits, to recognize the generally accepted narrow framework of scientic discourse, figured prominently in the last of the spirited scientific polemics he engaged in, the platinum controversy. Buffon had refused to acknowledge the recently discovered platinum as an authentic new metal, an element in its own right, because it was found in only a few places on the earth's surface: "It would be," he noted in another context (H.N.M. V, *"Traité de l'Aimant, article premier"*), "gravely to misunderstand the simplicity of the laws of nature to charge her with a tiny, isolated procedure," and, in the article on platinum (H.N.M. III), "All substances produced by the ordinary procedures of nature are widely distributed, at least in climates having similar temperatures: animals, plants, minerals, all are equally submissive to this universal rule." He argued that this rare new metal must therefore be an "accidental" product, most probably an alloy of iron and gold, an alloy unlike any other since it was a strangely permanent, seemingly unbreakable mix, doubtless produced under extraordinary "accidental" volcanic conditions that could not be duplicated in the laboratory and occurred only rarely in nature. His view was energetically—and a trifle spitefully—attacked by William (Don Guillermo) Bowles, an expatriate British lawyer from Cork who had become, through good fortune and patronage, the leading naturalist and the superintendent of mines in Spain: "If platinum, he [Bowles] says, 'were a composite of gold and iron,' as M. de Buffon claims, it ought to retain all the properties that result from that composition, and yet numerous experiments demonstrate the contrary" (quoted in H.M.N. III, *"De la Platine"*). Buffon, as always, elected to defend his position: "This skillful naturalist has failed to note that I expressly stated that the iron and the gold were not in their *ordinary* state, as in an artificial alloy" (H.N.M. III).

Buffon either could not or chose not to see that the average scientist's reaction to such an argument must be similar to that of a poker player who is unexpectedly informed that two of the cards in the deck are "wild." Scientific discourse, like poker, depends on rigid definition and complete predictability in the behavior of all units in play. It has little tolerance for verbal subtlety. By the end of the eighteenth century the scientific mentality was one that invariably recognized the primacy of demonstrated fact over attractive theory. The terminology, dominated by intractable fact, became rigid. Buffon, though, continued to see in scientific terminology the flexibility, the elasticity, that it had still possessed in his youth, an age of speculative science. He continued to bring to scientific discourse the habit of total intellectual receptivity toward the absolutely extraordinary, a sort of freewheeling "why not?" attitude, that was already being relegated to the domain of science fiction. His language, even at its most technical, has the amplitude, the looseness, of literary prose, language that places no shackles on the imagination. Any term can be dubbed "wild" if the successful completion of the pattern demands it.

V   *The Style Is the Man*

This review of a few of the outstanding features of Buffon's style—the compatibility of his thought with traditional rhetoric, his success at merging *ancien régime* dignity with ease and warmth, and the essentially belletristic character of even his most technical passages—leaves, as must any such review of the particular features of a style, the most important question unanswered: Why did this style impress so many astute judges as uniquely valuable? Why did T. S. Eliot find Buffon "delightful to read" and Jean-Jacques Rousseau, in a private letter, pronounce him *"la plus belle plume de son siècle,"* the finest prose stylist of the century? [15]

The answer might, of course, lie in precisely those qualities that translated passages cannot illustrate: a unique facility in phrasing, an impression of inevitable rightness in the wording, a rhythm that never seems false, never leaves an impression similar to that of a passage of music played in the wrong key or tempo. And certainly much of the pleasure one finds in reading Buffon stems from such qualities, evidence of the sureness of his literary taste, evidence that he possessed the "ear" of a born writer. Admiring critics often single out these tangible features;

for Sainte-Beuve, for example, "The genius of Buffon was as much
that of a poet as a philosopher; he combined, confounded, these
two characters within himself, much like the sages of ancient
times," and, again, *"il avait l'oreille, la mesure et le nombre."* [16]
But Buffon himself, in the *Discours sur le Style* and in private
remarks, attached little importance to these qualities, the stock-
in-trade of the poet.

To Buffon, as we have seen, a pervasive, absolute clarity was
the dominant factor. The impact of a style was identical with
the impact of the writer's mind. Style was not a manner of arrang-
ing words, but a manner of thinking, a vision of things. In brief,
the style was the man—and the spectrum of verbal techniques
employed merely the means by which the appeal of the man's
thought asserted itself, the medium rather than the thing itself.
If we accept Buffon's priorities, and an author is almost always
the best judge of the criteria that apply most aptly to his style,
we must conclude that the unique charm of Buffon's style, its
power to please, to provoke readers to exorbitant praise, lies in
the system of ideas for which it was the vehicle, and that in fact
it is his world view, the Buffonian world, that is "delightful."

It is a world of order, an organizing tendency everywhere triumphantly at work, arising out of the interplay of opposed forces
in whose opposition there seems to be always an element of com-
plicity. Buffon's rational "Nature," much like Bossuet's providen-
tial God, justifies a welcome, refreshing optimism. He presented
a vision of ultimate simplicity, a world that makes sense, a reality
centered around man's needs, responsive to his nature, and he
presented it, not in simplistic terms that would have repelled all
but the most naïve, but in a thousand ingenious demonstrations,
each one as exciting in itself as a successful chess maneuver, in-
terwoven throughout the fabric of an immense compendium of
verified facts. The appeal of his style was fundamentally intellectual. Perceptive critics who have examined Buffon's writing in
some depth, and once more Sainte-Beuve may serve as example,
have often arrived at "order"—the central preoccupation of Buffon's thought—as the essential trait of his style: "I do not know
how the idea has arisen that Buffon's style is overly emphatic:
it has only nobility, dignity, a magnificent suitability, a perfect
clarity. It is lofty, less by its movement and its surge, than by its
very persistence in an order that is always serious, always sus-

tained." [17] With few exceptions, the greatest admirers of Buffon's style have always been men to whom order, sometimes in other realms, was a paramount concern. The salient qualities of Buffon's mind—devotion to order, confidence, attention to detail, audacity in bridging gaps—are the qualities that constitute the central appeal of his great literary work, his vision, and his style.

Notes and References

Chapter Two

1. J. Y. T. Greig (ed.), *The Letters of David Hume* (Oxford, 1932), I, p. 530.
2. Mme E. Genet-Varcin and Jacques Roger, "Bibliographie de Buffon," items 305–54, in Jean Piveteau (ed.), *Oeuvres philosophiques de Buffon* (Paris, 1954).
3. Marie-Jean Hérault de Séchelles, *Voyage à Montbar* [*sic*] (Paris, An IX).
4. Robert Sage (ed. and trans.), *The Private Diaries of Stendhal* (Garden City, 1954), p. 404.
5. Henri Nadault de Buffon (ed.), *Correspondance de Buffon* (Paris, 1860), I, p. 218. Hereafter referred to as Nadault.
6. Fletcher Webster (ed.), *The Private Correspondence of Daniel Webster* (Boston, 1857), I, p. 371.

Chapter Three

1. Nadault, II, pp. 627, 628.
2. J.-L. de Lanessan (ed.), *Oeuvres complètes de Buffon . . . Suivie de la correspondance générale de Buffon, recueillie et annoté par M. Nadault de Buffon* (Paris, 1884–1885), XIV, p. 417. Hereafter referred to as Lanessan.
3. Hélène Monod-Cassidy, *Un Voyageur-Philosophe au XVIIIe siècle, l'abbé Jean-Bernard Le Blanc* (Cambridge, Mass., 1941), p. 192.
4. Françoise Weil, "La Correspondance Buffon-Cramer," *Revue d'Histoire des sciences et de leurs applications* (April, June, 1961), pp. 97–136.
5. The Manvers Archives of the University of Nottingham, England, MS 4355. Hickman's records do not always make clear whether the dating was "New Style" or "Old Style."
6. Slava Klima (ed.), "Spence's Travel Letters" (Unpublished dissertation, Yale University, 1955), p. 56.
7. *Journal de Paris*, May 3 and 4, 1788; reprinted in Lanessan, XIV, pp. 413–416. Ignace Bougot, "Notice sur la vie privée de M. le comte de Buffon," in Lanessan, XIV, pp. 405–12.

171

8. Hérault de Séchelles, *op. cit.*, pp. 32, 33.

9. Lanessan, XIV, p. 261, n. 1.

10. For detailed discussions of this very involved biographical question, see Stephen F. Milliken, "Buffon and the British" (Unpublished dissertation, Columbia University, 1965), pp. 109–53, and Lesley Hanks, *Buffon avant l' "Histoire Naturelle"* (Paris, 1966), pp. 253–58.

11. Gustave Michaut, "Buffon administrateur et homme d'affaires," *Annales de l'Université de Paris* (Jan.-Feb., 1931), pp. 5–36.

12. Léon Bertin, "Buffon homme d'affaires," in Roger Heim (ed.), *Buffon* (Paris, 1952), pp. 87–104.

13. Nadault, I, p. 361; Henri Nadault de Buffon (ed.), *Buffon, sa famille, ses collaborateurs et ses familiers, mémoires par M. Humbert-Bazile* (Paris, 1863), p. 373.

14. Bertin, *loc. cit.*, p. 93.

15. Nadault, I, p. 359.

16. Bertin, *loc. cit.*, p. 94.

17. *Ibid.*, p. 93.

18. Bibliothèque du Muséum d'Histoire Naturelle, Paris, MS 882, no. 37.

19. Nadault, II, p. 540.

Chapter Four

1. *Histoire de l'Académie Royale des Sciences . . . avec les mémoires de mathématique et de physique,* année 1733, pp. 43–45, 95–98.

2. Hanks, *op. cit.*, pp. 173, 183, 191, 213.

3. Jean-Bernard Le Blanc, *Letters on the English and French Nations . . . Translated from the Original French* (London, 1747), pp. 316, 317.

4. Theodore Besterman (ed.), *Voltaire's Correspondence* (Geneva, 1953–1965), IX, p. 246.

5. *Ibid.*, X, p. 305.

6. William F. Falls, *Buffon et l'agrandissement du Jardin du Roi à Paris* (Paris, 1933).

7. Daniel Mornet, *Les Sciences de la nature en France au XVIIIe siècle* (Paris, 1911), pp. 10, 11.

8. *Ibid.*, pp. 5–9.

9. Nadault, I, pp. 333–42.

10. Brémond d'Ars-Migré, *Un Collaborateur de Buffon, l'Abbé Bexon* (Paris, 1936).

11. Nadault, II, p. 38; Lanessan, XIII, p. 377.

12. Nadault, II, p. 33; Lanessan, XIII, p. 350; the ortolan, or sora, is a small, short-billed wading bird found in eastern North America.

13. Nadault, I, p. 319.

14. Nadault, II, p. 94.
15. Nadault, II, p. 200.
16. Hérault de Séchelles, *op. cit.*, p. 15.
17. Marie-Jean Antoine Nicolas Caritat, marquis de Condorcet, "Eloge de Buffon," in F. Cuvier (ed.), *Oeuvres complètes de Buffon* (Paris, 1829–1832), I, p. xlii.
18. Nadault, I, p. 369.
19. The *lettres patentes*, dated July, 1772, were registered in the Parlement of Burgundy on April 22, 1773, and in the Chambre des Comptes on June 9, 1774 (Nadault, I, p. 411).
20. Nadault, I, p. 464.
21. A. O. Aldridge, *Franklin and His French Contemporaries* (New York, 1957), p. 69.
22. J. W. Oliver, *The Life of William Beckford* (London, 1932), p. 188.
23. Jacques Necker (ed.), *Mélanges extraits des manuscrits de Mme Necker* (Paris, 1798), I, p. 87.
24. *Ibid.*, p. 327.

Chapter Five

1. The essay *La Théorie de la Terre*, although dated 1744, was first published in volume I of the *Histoire Naturelle* in 1749. The *Epoques de la Nature* appeared in the fifth volume of the *Suppléments* to the *Histoire Naturelle*, which bears the date 1778 on its title page. Jacques Roger, in his critical edition of the *Epoques*, established the exact dates of both the first public reading of the *Epoques* (August 5, 1773) and the first appearance in the bookstores of the fifth volume of *Suppléments* (August 10, 1779). Jacques Roger (ed.) *Buffon, Les Epoques de la Nature, Edition critique* (Paris, 1962), pp. xxxi, xxxvii, cxxix.
2. John Woodward, *An Essay towards a Natural History of the Earth* (3rd ed.; London, 1723), "The Preface."
3. John Ray, *Three Physico-Theological Discourses* (2nd ed.; London, 1693), p. 25.
4. Woodward, *op. cit.*, p. 8.
5. *Ibid.*, pp. 11, 90, 91, 93.
6. Sir Isaac Newton, *Principia*, ed. Florian Cajori (Berkeley, 1962), II, p. 522.
7. Vicq d'Azyr, "Eloge de Buffon," in *Oeuvres complètes de Buffon*, ed. F. Cuvier (Paris, 1829), I, p. lxxi.
8. M. le Chevalier Aude, *Vie privée du Comte de Buffon* (Lausanne, 1788), p. 9.
9. Pierre Flourens, *Des Manuscrits de Buffon* (Paris, 1860), pp. 64–72.
10. Lanessan, XIII, p. 78.

11. Charles Barthélemy, "La Religion de Buffon," *Erreurs et Mensonges historiques* (Paris, 1881), Sixième Série, pp. 94–117.

12. Jean Piveteau, "La Pensée religieuse de Buffon," in Heim, *op. cit.*, pp. 125–32.

13. *Revue d'Histoire littéraire de la France*, XLII, p. 150.

14. Lanessan, XIII, p. 142.

15. Lanessan, XIII, pp. 125, 126, 140, 154, 155.

Chapter Six

1. T. N. (John Turberville Needham), *An Account of Some New Microscopical Discoveries* (London, 1745), p. 104. Hereafter referred to as Needham, 1745.

2. Needham, 1745, pp. 2, 3.

3. Needham, 1745, p. 86; *Philosophical Transactions of the Royal Society of London*, XLII, No. 471, p. 634 ff; C. Hutton (ed.), G. Shaw (ed.), and R. Pearson (ed.), *The Philosophical Transactions of the Royal Society of London . . . Abridged* (London, 1809), VII, 729 ff.

4. Needham, 1745, p. 5 ff, 12, 13.

5. Needham, 1745, p. 41.

6. Needham, 1745, p. 56.

7. Needham, 1745, p. 62.

8. Nadault, I, p. 29; Lanessan, XIII, p. 40.

9. Francis Darwin (ed.), *The Life and Letters of Charles Darwin* (New York, 1959), II, pp. 228–29.

10. M. de Needham (John Turberville Needham), M. l'Abbé Spallanzani and M. l'Abbé Regley, *Nouvelles recherches sur les découvertes microscopiques* (Paris and London, 1769), I, pp. 220–26. Hereafter referred to as Needham, 1769.

11. *Philosophical Transactions of the Royal Society of London*, XLIV, N. 481 (1746), pp. 257–58.

12. Erik Nordenskiöld, *The History of Biology* (New York, 1928), p. 225, n. 3.

13. Turberville Needham (John Turberville Needham), *Observations upon the Generation, Composition, and Decomposition of Animal and Vegetable Substances* (London, 1749), p. 21. Hereafter referred to as Needham, 1749.

14. Needham, 1749, p. 30.

15. Needham, 1769, I, pp. 142, 165, 166, 190, 265, 267.

16. *The Monthly Review*, LVI (1777), 512–14; Benjamin C. Nangle, *The Monthly Review, First Series, 1749–1789; Indexes of Contributors and Articles* (Oxford, 1934), I, pp. 28, 108.

17. *The Monthly Review*, LXX (June, 1784), 525; Nangle, *op. cit.*, I, p. 108.

18. Needham, 1749, p. 40; cf. H.N. II, p. 304.

19. Needham, 1749, p. 1; Needham, 1769, I, p. xliv. M. Needham (John Turberville Needham), *Nouvelles observations microscopiques* (Paris, 1750), pp. ix, x. Hereafter referred to as Needham, 1750.

20. Needham, 1750, pp. ix, x, 259; cf. Needham, 1769, I, xlii.

21. *Mémoires de l'Académie Impériale et Royale des Sciences et Belles-Lettres de Bruxelles*, IV, Année 1783, p. xxxvii.

22. Needham, 1749, p. 31.

23. Needham, 1750, p. 303.

24. Needham, 1769, I, pp. 10, 211, 212, 217.

25. Needham, 1750, pp. 411, 451, 452.

26. Needham, 1750, pp. 275, 320, 334, 441, 450; Needham, 1769, I, p. 148.

27. Needham, 1750, pp. 277–79.

28. Needham, 1750, pp. 315, 374; Needham, 1769, I, pp. 150–56, 161–72, 232–33.

29. Needham, 1769, I, p. 232.

30. Frank Brady (ed.) and Frederick A. Pottle (ed.), *Boswell on the Grand Tour, Italy, Corsica, and France, 1765–1766* (New York, Toronto, London, 1955), p. 30.

31. Chauncy Brewster Tinker (ed.), *Letters of James Boswell* (Oxford, 1924), I, p. 238.

32. François-Marie Arouet de Voltaire, *Oeuvres complètes de Voltaire* (Paris, 1876–1878), VIII, 706.

33. *Ibid.*, VIII, 699–702.

34. Nadault, I, p. 115; Lanessan, XIII, p. 170.

35. Voltaire, *op. cit.*, V, 116.

36. *Ibid.*, V, 836.

Chapter Seven

1. Nadault, II, p. 16; Lanessan, XIII, p. 38; cf. Nadault, II, p. 256.

2. Samuel Butler, *Evolution, Old and New* (New York, 1911), p. 31.

3. *Ibid.*, p. 63.

4. *Ibid.*, pp. 81, 84.

5. *Ibid.*, p. 89.

6. *Ibid.*, p. 112.

7. Loren Eiseley, *Darwin's Century* (Garden City, New York, 1961), p. 45.

8. J. S. Wilkie, "The Idea of Evolution in the Writings of Buffon," *Annals of Science*, XIII, No. 1 (March, 1956), No. 3 (September, 1956), 48–63, 212–27, 255–66.

9. *Ibid.*, p. 48.

10. Jacques Roger, *Epoques*, op. cit., pp. xxiii, lxviii; Jacques Roger, *Les Sciences de la vie dans la pensée française du XVIIIe siècle* (Armand Colin, 1963), pp. 558–84.

11. Roger, *Sciences, op. cit.*, p. 566.

12. Wilkie, *op. cit.*, pp. 213–15, 220, 259.

13. John C. Greene, *The Death of Adam, Evolution and Its Impact on Western Thought* (New York, 1961), pp. 142–60, 251, 269, 271, 282–83; cf. "Animaux communs aux deux continens" in H.N. IX.

14. Roger, *Sciences, op. cit.*, pp. 566–84.

15. Condorcet, *loc. cit.*, p. xviii.

16. Wilkie, *op. cit.*, pp. 255–58.

17. Roger, *Sciences, op. cit.*, pp. 577–84.

18. Pierre Teilhard de Chardin, *The Phenomenon of Man,* trans. Bernard Wall (New York and Evanston, 1961), p. 216.

19. Wilkie, *op. cit.*, p. 48.

20. *Ibid.,* p. 51.

21. Roger, *Sciences, op. cit.*, p. 582.

Chapter Eight

1. Nadault, I, p. 379.

2. Etienne Bonnot de Condillac, *Traité des Animaux* (Amsterdam, 1755), pp. 66, 83, 189.

3. *Ibid.,* pp. 21, 201.

4. *Ibid.,* p. 85.

5. *Ibid.,* pp. 70, 80, 85–87, 153, 180–81.

6. Walter Scheidt, "The Concept of Race in Anthropology and the Division into Human Races from Linnaeus to Deniker," in Earl W. Count (ed.), *This Is Race* (New York, 1950), p. 360.

7. Piveteau, *Oeuvres, op. cit.*, p. xxiv.

8. Hérault de Séchelles, *op. cit.*, p. 29.

9. Lanessan, XIII, p. 298, 304 ff; XIV, pp. 41, 146.

10. Nadault, I, p. 429; Lanessan, XIII, pp. 225, 226, 229.

11. Nadault, II, p. 464.

12. Louis Dimier, *Buffon* (Paris, 1919), p. 219.

13. Nadault, I, p. 258, 274; II, p. 383.

14. Otis Fellows, "Buffon's Place in the Enlightenment," *Studies on Voltaire and the Eighteenth Century* (Transactions of the First International Congress on the Enlightenment, XXIV/XXVII) (Geneva, 1963), pp. 610, 611. Cf. Jacques Roger, "Diderot et Buffon en 1749," *Diderot Studies,* IV 1963), 221–36; Otis Fellows, "Buffon and Rousseau: Aspects of a Relationship," *PMLA,* LXXV, No. 3 (June, 1960), 184–96.

15. Nadault, I, pp. 227, 231.

16. Carl Van Doren (ed.), *Benjamin Franklin's Autobiographical Writings* (New York, 1945), p. 750.

17. William F. Falls, "Buffon, Franklin, et Deux Académies Américaines," *Romanic Review,* XXIX (1938), 40, 42.

18. Edwin T. Martin, *Thomas Jefferson: Scientist* (New York, 1961), p. 150.

19. Milliken, *op. cit.*, p. 467.

20. Martin, *op. cit.*, pp. 99, 100, 146, 156–62.

21. Otis Fellows, "Voltaire and Buffon: Clash and Conciliation," *Symposium*, IX, No. 2 (Fall, 1955), 234.

Chapter Nine

1. T. S. Eliot, "Religion and Literature," *Essays Ancient and Modern* (New York, 1936), pp. 94, 95.

2. Emile Faguet, *XVIIIe siècle, études littéraires* (Paris, n.d.), p. 486.

3. As quoted in Rene Wellek and Austin Warren, *Theory of Literature* (New York, 1949), p. 76.

4. Charles de Gaulle, *The War Memoirs of Charles de Gaulle*, trans. Richard Howard (New York, 1960), p. 103.

5. Piveteau, *Oeuvres, op. cit.*, p. 510; Nadault, I, p. 23; Lanessan, XIII, p. 95.

6. Roger, *Epoques, op. cit.*, p. cix, n. 2.

7. This argument for the illustrative value of translated passages, based on an appeal to the uniquely intellectual and methodical character of much of Buffon's writing, is not expected to meet with very general agreement. Surely, the counter argument runs, the losses involved in translation are insurmountable, can never be dismissed, and should never be minimized. It is offered only as a necessary rationale for what is in any case an inevitable expedient.

8. Nadault, I, p. 226.

9. Nadault, I, p. 474.

10. Nadault, I, p. 255.

11. Nadault, I, p. 380.

12. Nadault, II, p. 321.

13. Nadault, I, p. 308.

14. Roger, *op. cit.*, pp. cxiv–cxxvii.

15. Théophile Dufour (ed.) and Pierre-Paul Plan (ed.), *Correspondance générale de Jean-Jacques Rousseau* (Paris, 1924–1934), XII, 25.

16. Charles-Augustin Sainte-Beuve, *Causeries du lundi* (Paris, 1857), IV, 351, 362.

17. *Ibid.*, IV, 362.

Selected Bibliography

PRIMARY SOURCES

BUFFON, GEORGES-LOUIS LECLERC, COMTE DE. *Histoire Naturelle, Générale et Particulière, avec la description du Cabinet du Roi.* 44 vols. in 4°. Paris: De l'Imprimerie Royale, puis Plassans, 1749–1804. Still usable, still available; an impressive testimonial to the remarkable durability of books printed on paper of the best quality in the eighteenth century.

———— (trans.). *La Statique des Végétaux, et l'analyse de l'air,* 2nd ed., in Joseph-Aignan Sigaud de La Fond (ed.), *La Statique des Végétaux et celle des animaux . . . par le D. Hales.* Paris: De l'Imprimerie de Monsieur, 1779. The translator's preface marks an important stage in the early evolution of Buffon's thought.

———— (trans.). *La Méthode des Fluxions et des suites infinies. Par M. le Chevalier Newton.* Paris: Chez De Bure l'aîné, 1740. Also notable mainly for the translator's preface.

————. *Correspondance Inédite de Buffon, à laquelle ont été réunies les lettres publiées jusqu'à ce jour.* Edited by Henri Nadault de Buffon. 2 vols. Paris: L. Hachette et Cie, 1860. The excellent and very copious notes of this first edition were drastically reduced in the Lanessan edition.

————. *Oeuvres complètes de Buffon . . . suivies de la correspondance générale de Buffon, recueillie et annotée par M. Nadault de Buffon.* Edited by J.-L. de Lanessan and Henri Nadault de Buffon. 14 vols. Paris: A. Le Vasseur, 1884–1885. Very few copies of this edition were printed, and it is not generally available.

————. *Oeuvres philosophiques de Buffon.* ("Corpus général des philosophes français, auteurs modernes," t. XLI, 1.) Edited by Jean Piveteau. Paris: Presses Universitaires de France, 1954. The best book through which to approach Buffon, containing generous selections from his writings, critical articles by Jean Piveteau, Charles Bruneau, and Maurice Fréchet, and a Buffon bibliography with more than a thousand entries (items 84–104 list Buffon's early contributions to the *Mémoires* of the Académie Royale), compiled by Jacques Roger and Mme E. Genet-Varcin.

179

————. *Les Epoques de la Nature, Edition critique.* ("Mémoires du Muséum National d'Histoire Naturelle, Nouvelle Série," Série X.) Edited by Jacques Roger. Paris: Editions du Muséum, 1962. Jacques Roger's very long introduction is the most authoritative discussion of Buffon's cosmogony.

SECONDARY SOURCES

AUDE, M. LE CHEVALIER. *Vie privée du comte de Buffon.* Lausanne, 1788. Short, and meandering, but it does offer personal glimpses into the daily life of the Montbard château late in Buffon's life.

BUTLER, SAMUEL. *Evolution, Old and New, or the Theories of Buffon, Dr. Erasmus Darwin and Lamarck, as compared with that of Charles Darwin.* 3rd ed. revised. New York: E. P. Dutton and Company, 1911. The arguments are extreme, and dubious, but the presentation is dazzling.

CONDILLAC, ETIENNE BONNOT DE. *Traité des Animaux.* Amsterdam, 1755. The most worthwhile of the contemporary critiques of Buffon.

CONDORCET, MARIE-JEAN ANTOINE NICOLAS CARITAT, MARQUIS DE. "Eloge de Buffon," in F. Cuvier (ed.), *Oeuvres complètes de Buffon* (Paris: F.-D. Pillot, 1829–1832), I, v–xlvi. A brilliantly eloquent piece; Buffon seen through the eyes of a contemporary who detested him.

DIMIER, LOUIS. *Buffon.* Paris: Nouvelle Librairie Nationale, 1919. A professional biography, but excessively argumentative, using Buffon as a case in point to extol the virtues of conservatism and nationalism.

FALLS, WILLIAM FRANKLIN. *Buffon et l'agrandissement du Jardin du Roi à Paris.* (Reprint from *Archives du Muséum*, 6e Série, t. X, 1933.) Paris: Masson et Cie, 1933. A step-by-step retracing of the development of a great institution under Buffon's management.

FELLOWS, ÓTIS. "Voltaire and Buffon: Clash and Conciliation," *Symposium*, IX, No. 2 (Fall, 1955), 222–35. A battle of egos, conducted with noblesse oblige.

————. "Buffon and Rousseau: Aspects of a Relationship," *PMLA*, LXXV, No. 3 (June, 1960), 184–96. A study in contrasting temperaments and parallel ideas.

————. "Buffon's Place in the Enlightenment," *Studies on Voltaire and the Eighteenth Century* (Transactions of the First International Congress on the Enlightenment), XXIV/XXVII; Geneva: Institut et Musée Voltaire, 1963, pp. 603–29. A succinct overview.

————. "Encore un Détracteur de Buffon," in Werner Bahner, ed., *Beiträge zur Französischen Aufklärung und zur Spanischen Litera-*

tur. Festgabe für Werner Krauss zum 70. Geburtstag. (Berlin: Akademie-Verlag, 1971).

GEOFFROY SAINT-HILAIRE, ETIENNE. *Fragments biographiques de Buffon.* Paris: F. D. Pillot, 1838. An exalted view of Buffon's powers as a thinker.

HANKS, LESLEY. *Buffon avant l' "Histoire Naturelle."* ("Publications de la Faculté des Lettres et Sciences humaines de Paris," Série "Recherches," t. XXIV.) Paris: Presses Universitaires de France, 1966. An ample treatment of Buffon's apprentice years.

HEIM, ROGER (ed.). *Buffon.* ("Les Grands Naturalistes Français.") Paris: Le Muséum National d'Histoire Naturelle, 1952. Ten articles of uniform excellence, including Léon Bertin on Buffon as a businessman and Jean Piveteau on his religious views.

HÉRAULT DE SÈCHELLES, MARIE-JEAN. *Voyage à Montbar.* Paris: Solvet, An IX. A rare journalistic talent at work.

MILLIKEN, STEPHEN F. "Buffon and the British." Unpublished Ph.D. dissertation, Columbia University, 1965. Detailed treatments of biographical problems; a number of Buffon's letters are edited here that are not listed elsewhere.

NADAULT DE BUFFON, HENRI. *Buffon, sa famille, ses collaborateurs, et ses familiers, mémoires par M. Humbert-Bazile.* Paris: Renouard, 1863. Much useful information throughout, and some of the original material by Humbert-Bazile, Buffon's secretary, is fascinating, but the book's value is complicated by Nadault's "imaginative" editing, filling gaps with material lifted from Aude and Hérault.

ROGER, JACQUES. *Les Sciences de la vie dans la pensée française du XVIII⁰ siècle.* Armand Colin, 1963. Chapter II of Part III on Buffon is the most authoritative discussion of Buffon as a biological theorist.

SAINTE-BEUVE, CHARLES-AUGUSTIN. *Causeries du lundi.* Paris: Garnier Frères, 1857. A great critic, who approached Buffon's work with extraordinary sympathy.

WEIL, FRANÇOISE. "La Correspondance Buffon-Cramer," *Revue d'Histoire des sciences et de leurs Applications,* XIV, No. 2 (Avril–Juin, 1961), 97–136. The young Buffon as a neophyte mathematician.

WILKIE, J. S. "The Idea of Evolution in the Writings of Buffon," *Annals of Science,* XII, No. 1 (March, 1956), 48–63, No. 3 (September, 1957), 212–27, 255–66. The definitive discussion of Buffon and Evolution.

Index

Adam, 125–29, 133, 134
Adams, John, 18
Aldridge, A. O., 173 n. 21
Les Animaux Sauvages, 155
Archimedes, 57
Aristotle, 23, 95, 121, 137, 138
Aude, Chevalier, 29, 74, 173 n. 8

Bacon, Francis, 18, 19, 32, 53, 98
Barre, Chevalier de la, 83
Barthélemy, Charles, 83, 84, 174 n. 11
Baudelaire, Charles, 149
Bayle, Pierre, 56
Beckford, William, 64, 173 n. 22
Bertin, Léon, 48, 172 n. 4
Besterman, Theodore, 172 n. 4
Bexon, Abbé Gabriel, 57, 58
Billarderie d'Angeviller, Comte de la, 62
Bois-St-Just, Marquis de, 40
Bonnet, Charles, 97
Bossuet, Jacques Bénique, 136
Boswell, James, 107
Bougainville, Louis-Antoine de, 142
Bougot, Ignace, 43, 44, 45, 65, 171 n. 7
Boulanger, Nicolas-Antoine, 82
Boulduc, Gilles-François, 51
Bourguet, Louis, 70
Bowles, William, 167
Brady, Frank, 175 n. 30
Brosse, Charles de, 84, 108
Bruce, James, 142
Buffon, Chevalier de (half-brother of Buffon), 40, 44, 47

Buffon, Georges-Louis Leclerc, Comte de (Buffon *himself*)
Buffonet (son of Buffon), 30, 44, 61, 62, 63, 123
Burnet, Thomas, 67, 68, 81
Bute, John S., 56
Butler, Samuel, 115–19, 122, 124, 175 n. 2
Byron, Lord, 28

Cabeen, D. C., 16
Caesar, Julius, 80
Cajori, Florian, 173 n. 6
Catherine the Great, 33, 56, 62
Cepoy, Marquis de, 63
Chambers, Robert, 115
Chastellux, Marquis de, 36
Chateaubriand, François René, Vicomte de, 83
Châtelet, Marquise de, 53
Cheselden, William, 131
Clairaut, Alexis, 41
Condillac, Abbé Etienne Bonnot de, 129, 130, 131, 133, 145, 157, 176 n. 2
Condorcet, Antoine N., Marquis de, 44, 61, 121, 173 n. 17, 176 n. 15
Cook, James, 142
Count, Earl W., 176 n. 6
Cramer, Gabriel, 41
Cronstedt, Axel Fredrik, 165
Cuvier, F., 173 n. 17

D'Alembert, Jean le Rond, 28, 145
D'Ars-Migré, Brémond, 172 n. 10
Darwin, Charles, 98, 112, 115, 116, 118, 119, 122, 174 n. 9

Darwin, Erasmus, 115, 123
Darwin, Francis, 174 n. 9
Daubenton, Betzy, 63
Daubenton, Edme, 57, 60
Daubenton, Mme Georges-Louis, 144
Daubenton, Louis, 57, 58, 59, 63, 102
Descartes, René, 18, 19, 20, 23, 53, 57, 67, 73, 92, 108, 132, 134, 161
Destouches, Philippe N., 28
Diderot, Denis, 16, 17, 18, 21, 23, 24, 58, 63, 145
Dimier, Louis, 145, 176 n. 12
Discours sur la Nature des Animaux, 33, 34
Discours sur le Style, 22, 149–54, 155, 163, 169
Dodun, Abbé François-Charles, 143
Dufay, Charles-François de Cisternay, 54, 55
Dufour, Théophile, 177 n. 15
Duhamel du Monceau, Henri-Louis, 51, 52, 54

Eiseley, Loren, 118, 175 n. 7
Eliot, T. S., 148, 168, 177 n. 1
Empedocles, 115
De l'Enfance, 139, 140
Epinay, Louise F. P. La Live d', 64
Epoques de la Nature, 26, 66, 69–84, 114, 119, 161, 162, 173 n. 1
Essai d'Arithmétique morale, 49

Faguet, Emile, 148, 177 n. 2
Falls, William F., 172 n. 6, 176 n. 17
Faujas de Saint-Fond, Barthélemy, 59
Feller, Abbé François-Xavier de, 83
Fellows, Otis, 176 n. 14, 177 n. 21
Flourens, Pierre, 75, 173 n. 9
Folkes, Martin, 101
Fontenelle, Bernard Le Bovier de, 51
Franklin, Benjamin, 18, 56, 146
Frederick the Great, 57
Freud, Sigmund, 19, 151

Gaulle, Charles de, 152, 177 n. 4
Genesis, 75, 81, 84
Genet-Varcin, E., 171 n. 2
Geoffrin, Marie Thérèse, 64
Godard, 44, 45
Graaf, Reinier de, 91, 101
Greene, John C., 176 n. 13
Greig, J. Y. T., 171 n. 1
Grimm, Friedrich Melchior, 62, 129
Gueneau de Montbeillard, Philibert, 57, 58, 59, 61
Guillemin, 60

Hales, Stephen, 52, 110
Hanks, Lesley, 172 n. 10, 172, n. 2
Harvey, William, 91
Hellot, Jean, 54
Helvétius, Claude-Adrien, 23, 53, 54, 145
Henry of Prussia, 33
Hérault de Séchelles, Marie-Jean, 30–39, 44, 45, 60, 83, 137, 149
Herodotus, 137
Hickman, Nathan, 41, 42, 43, 46, 70
Hill, John, 89
Histoire Naturelle de l'Homme, 125, 143
Histoire Naturelle des Minéraux, 59, 112, 159, 162, 163, 164
Histoire Naturelle des Oiseaux, 59, 112
Histoire Naturelle des Quadrupèdes, 112
Holbach, Paul H. T., Baron d', 23, 65, 84, 146
De l'Homme, 139, 140
Homo Duplex, 130, 134, 135, 136
Humbert-Bazile, 29, 48, 61, 62, 83
Hume, David, 28
Huxley, T. H., 98

Ignace (*see* Bougot)

Jalabert, Jean, 99
Jefferson, Thomas, 18, 36, 56, 80, 146
Johnson, Samuel, 28

Kant, Immanuel, 21
Keill, John, 67, 76
Kingston, Duke of, 41, 42, 43, 45, 46, 47, 70
Klima, Slava, 171 n. 6

Lacépède, Bernard Germain, Comte de, 59, 60
Lalande, Joseph J. Lefrançais de, 64
Lamarck, Jean Baptiste, Chevalier de, 62, 115, 123
La Touche, Mme de, 43
Le Blanc, Jean-Bernard, 40, 53, 62, 82, 172 n. 3
Le Brun, Dominique, 144
Lebrun, Echouard, 157
Leclerc (family), 47, 63
Leclerc, Anne-Madeleine, 47
Leclerc, Benjamin-François, 40, 46
Leclerc, Charles-Benjamin, 47
Leclerc, Jeanne, 47, 61
Leeuwenhoek, Antony van, 87, 89, 99
Leibnitz, 32
Linnaeus, 26, 95, 119, 121, 165
Locke, John, 18, 19, 125, 128, 129, 133, 134
Louis XV of France, 57
Lucretius, 23

MacLaine, Archibald, 104
Maillet, Benoît de, 109, 115
Mairan, Dortous de, 76, 77
Malpighi, Marcello, 91
Mandonnet, Nicolas-Dominique, 144
Mann, Abbé, 104
Marmontel, Jean-François, 157
Martin, Edwin T., 177 n. 18
Marriage, 138
Marx, Karl, 19
Maupertuis, Pierre-Louis Moreau de, 98
Maurepas, Jean F. P., Comte de, 51, 54, 56
Mémoire sur la Conservation . . . des Forêts, 51
Mémoire sur un moyen . . . d'augmenter . . . la durée du Bois, 51

Mémoire sur la Culture des Forêts, 51
Michaut, Gustave, 172 n. 11
"Micromégas fallacy," 88
Milliken, Stephen F., 172 n. 10, 177 n. 19
Le Moineau, 159
Monod-Cassidy, Hélène, 171 n. 3
Montaigne, Michel de, 136
Montesquieu, Charles Louis de Secondat, 16, 17, 18, 20, 24, 32, 38, 82, 150
Mornet, Daniel, 55, 56, 172 n. 7
Moses, 82

Nadault de Buffon, Henri, 29, 30, 33, 44, 83, 145, 156
Nangle, Benjamin C., 174 n. 16
Natural Law, 137, 138, 141, 142
De la Nature des Animaux, 134
De la Nature de l'Homme, 131, 142
Necker, Jacques, 173 n. 23
Necker, Suzanne Curchod, 59, 64, 65
Needham, John Turberville, 60, 86–111, 112, 114, 174 n. 1
Newton, Sir Isaac, 18, 19, 20, 32, 33, 53, 66, 73, 74, 75, 76, 95, 105, 108, 173 n. 6
Noah, 67
Nordskiöld, Eric, 102, 174 n. 12
Nymphomania, 137–38

Oliver, J. W., 173 n. 22
Orléans, Louis Philippe Joseph Duc d', 63
Ostoya, Paul, 119

Pajou, Augustin, 63
Le Pigeon, 160
Piron, Alexis, 149
Pirri, Filippo, 113
Pitt, William, 56
Piveteau, Jean, 83, 136, 174 n. 12, 176 n. 7, 177 n. 5
Plan, Pierre-Paul, 177 n. 15
De la Platine, 167
Plato, 23, 79, 95, 156
Pliny the Elder, 23, 137, 156

Pompadour, Marquise de, 34
Pottle, Frederick A., 175 n. 30
Preuves de la Théorie de la Terre,
  72
Preuves de la Théorie de la Terre,
  Additions et Corrections, 71
Psalmanazar, George, 141
De la Puberté, 139, 143

Ray, John, 69, 76, 95, 173 n. 3
Regley, Abbé, 174 n. 10
Rochon, Abbé, 163
Roger, Jacques, 26, 119, 121, 122,
  123, 162, 173 n. 1, 175 n. 10,
  176 n. 11, 177 n. 15
Rostand, Jean, 119
Rousseau, Jean-Jacques, 15, 16, 17,
  18, 23, 24, 38, 140, 145, 149, 168,
  177 n. 15
Royou, Abbé Thomas-Marie, 83
Ruffey, Gilles-Germain Richard de,
  42, 43, 46, 51, 61

Sage, Robert, 171 n. 4
Saint-Belin, Abbé de, 143, 144
Saint-Belin-Malin, Marie-Françoise,
  61, 143
Sainte-Beuve, Charles A., 16, 17,
  148, 168, 169, 177 n. 15
Scheidt, Walter, 136, 176 n. 6
Des Sels, 160
Du Soufre, 166
Des Stalactites cristallisées du Quartz,
  163, 165
Stalactites vitreuses, 166
Sens, Archbishop of, 149
Des Sens en général, 125
Du Sens de la Vue, 130, 131
Shaw, George Bernard, 19, 118
Scotus, Duns, 19
Smellie, William, 98
Solutions de Problèmes sur le jeu
  du franc-carreau, 51
Soulavie, Abbé, 64
Spallanzani, Lazzaro, 103, 105, 113,
  174 n. 10

Spence, Joseph, 42, 43
Stael, Germaine Necker, Baronne de,
  65
Stendhal, 31
Stormont, 65
Suppléments, 22, 51, 67, 112, 113,
  149, 173 n. 1

Teilhard de Chardin, Pierre, 84, 122,
  176 n. 18
Théorie de la Terre, 26, 66, 69, 70,
  73, 74, 78, 109, 112, 173 n. 1
Thouin, André, 49, 57, 60
Tillich, Paul, 19
Tinker, Chauncey Brewster, 175 n.
  31
Traité de l'Aimant, 164, 166, 167
Traité des Animaux, 129
Traité des Sensations, 129
Tremblay, Abraham, 88

Valisnieri, Antonio, 91
Van Doran, Carl, 176 n. 16
Variétés dans l'Espèce humaine, 141,
  142, 147
Vénus physique, 98
Vercingetorix, 80
Verley, Frédérique C., 3
Vicq d'Azyr, 74, 173 n. 7
Voltaire, F. Marie Arouet de, 16, 17,
  18, 19, 24, 53, 54, 62, 63, 81, 87,
  107, 108, 109, 119, 145, 146, 150,
  157, 174 n. 32
Vue de la Nature, 84

Wall, Bernard, 176 n. 18
Warren, Austin, 177 n. 7
Webster, Daniel, 36
Webster, Fletcher, 171 n. 4
Wellek, Rene, 177 n. 3
Whiston, William, 68, 69, 81
Wilkie, J. S. 118–23, 175 n. 8, 176
  n. 12
Woodward, John, 68, 69, 70, 71, 81,
  110, 173 n. 2